Washington Real Estate Fundamentals Workbook

Third Edition

Rockwell Publishing Company

By Rockwell Publishing Company
13218 N.E. 20th Street
Bellevue, WA 98005
(206) 747-7272

ISBN: 1-887051-05-8

PRINTED IN CANADA

Table of Contents

Introduction

This workbook is for use in conjunction with the inGenious computer-based learning system for Washington Real Estate Fundamentals. From time to time in each lesson, you will be asked to complete a series of exercises that will test your comprehension. When the program instructs you to do so, complete the appropriate exercise in this workbook. When you have finished an exercise, check your answers using the answer key at the back of the workbook.

The inGenious system is interactive; it invites you to actively participate in the learning process. In addition to the workbook exercises, you will be asked to solve problems presented on the computer screen in a variety of formats. Simple instructions will be given for each problem. No computer skills are required.

At the end of each lesson, you're required to take a Lesson Quiz. The multiple-choice questions for each quiz are printed here in the workbook. When you've decided on your answers, you will enter them on the answer sheet that appears on the computer screen at the end of the lesson. When you press the "Grade Quiz" button on the screen, inGenious will instantly score your answers. It will tell you if you missed any questions, and if so, which ones. It's a good idea to review any areas that have given you trouble (in your textbook or on the computer) before going on to the next lesson.

The first time you use inGenious, the program will start off with a tutorial showing how the system works. You'll also find a section called "How to Use inGenious" here in the workbook, on the pages immediately following this introduction. In addition to basic operating instructions, it includes some important information about the steps you must take in order to receive credit for this course. Please be sure to read it before you begin.

How to Use inGenious

This section includes some basic operating instructions for the inGenious system, and also information about the steps you must take to receive credit for the course.

1. Turn the computer on. The on/off switch is usually on the front of the computer box. It may also be necessary to turn the monitor (the viewing screen) on separately. The on/off switch for the monitor may be below the screen on the front of the monitor, or it may be on the back of the monitor.

2. Insert the inGenious CD. Put the inGenious compact disk into the computer's CD ROM drive. The drive is one of the slots on the front of the computer box, or else a separate unit attached to the computer.

3. Start Windows. On some computers, Microsoft Windows will start automatically when the computer is turned on. If that happens, you can go directly on to step 4. Otherwise, you can start Windows when the DOS prompt appears on your screen. The DOS prompt looks like this: C:\>. Simply type "WIN" beside the prompt and then press the Enter key on your keyboard. (The Enter key is called the Return key on some keyboards.)

4. Learn to use the mouse. When Windows first opens, it will start you off in the Program Manager. To get from the Program Manager to inGenious, you'll have to learn to use the **mouse**. The mouse is the device attached to your computer that looks like this:

Like the keyboard, the mouse allows you to communicate with the computer. On the bottom of the mouse, there's a ball that will roll on a smooth surface like your desktop. By rolling the mouse across your desktop, you can move the **cursor** — the small arrow that appears on the computer screen — in order to point to different items on the screen. Roll the mouse to the left or the right, and the cursor will move to the left or the right on the screen. Roll the mouse away from you, and the cursor will move up the screen. Roll the mouse toward you, and the cursor will move down the screen.

Once the cursor is pointing at an item you want to activate, to select that item, you **click** on it: press the left mouse button down and then release it. In some cases, it is necessary to **double click** on an item to select it: quickly press and release the left mouse button <u>twice</u>. Once you've had a little practice using the mouse, it will be easy for you.

5. Open the inGenious window. Across the top of the Program Manager screen, you'll see a row of words (File; Options; Window; Help); this is called the **menu bar**. Using your mouse, point the cursor at the word "Window" in the menu bar at the top of the screen. Click the left mouse button to open that menu. When the menu drops open, you'll see that inGenious is one of the choices listed. Use the mouse to point the cursor at inGenious, and then click on it (press the left mouse button once and release it) to open the inGenious window.

6. Start inGenious. In the inGenious window, you'll see the inGenious icon. An icon is a little picture on the computer screen that identifies a program. The inGenious icon is a picture of a stack of books.

Use the mouse to double click (quickly press and release the left mouse button twice) on the inGenious icon to start the program.

7. Log in. When you double click on the inGenious icon, a **dialog box** appears on the screen. It's called a "dialog" box because the computer is asking you to talk to it — to give it certain information. In this case, the computer wants you to enter your name and social security number.

The cursor automatically appears in the "Name" box, so go ahead and type in your name. Next press the Tab key on your keyboard to move the cursor into the "Social Security Number" box, then type your social security number. This is how inGenious will keep track of the time you spend working in the program and your test scores, so it's essential to type in the same number every time you use the program. Once you've entered the required information, use the mouse to click on the OK button on the screen.

8. Logging in for the first time. The first time you log in, a second dialog box will appear, asking you for additional information: your address and phone number.

Fill in each of these boxes, using the Tab key on your keyboard to move the cursor from one box to the next, (If you need to move back into a box after you've left it, you can press the Tab key while holding down the Shift key. Or you can simply move the cursor into any of the boxes with the mouse.) Once you've filled in all the requested information, use the mouse to press the OK button. (If you want to leave the program, press the Cancel button instead.)

When you log in for the first time, inGenious starts with a brief tutorial that will help you get started with the program. Initially, the progarm will advance from one screen to the next automatically, allowing you 30 seconds to read each screen. Then follow the instructions shown on the screen to work through the tutorial.

Note: The second dialog box (asking for your address and phone number) and the tutorial should only appear the first time you use inGenious. If you see these when you log in on any subsequent occasion, it may mean that you entered your social security number incorrectly, so you should start over. While the second dialog box is on the screen, select the Cancel button in the dialog box. Then restart inGenious (step 6, above) and enter your social security number again. If the tutorial starts before you realize there's a problem, finish the tutorial; but do not start a lesson when the tutorial ends. Instead, select the Exit button on the Lesson Menu, then restart inGenious and enter your social security number again. Otherwise you won't receive credit for your session.

9. Choosing a lesson. After the tutorial (or, if you've used the program before, right after you log in), the screen with the Lesson Menu appears. Use the mouse to press the button for the lesson you want to work on, and the lesson will automatically begin.

10. Moving through a lesson. Within the lesson, there are 3 buttons in the lower right hand corner of each screen.

Each screen in the lesson will stay on as long as you want it to. When you've finished reading, you can move on to the next screen by using the mouse to press the Forward button — the button with the arrow pointing right. (If you ever want to go back to an earlier screen, press the Reverse button — the one with the arrow pointing left.)

The oval button will bring up three additional buttons. An Exit button, a Glossary button, and a Calculator button. The Exit button will return you to Windows.

11. Hotwords and the Glossary. In many frames, you'll see that certain words in the text appear in red. That means those words are **hotwords**. By using the mouse to click on a hotword, you can activate the Glossary. A definition of the hotword will appear on the screen. When you've finished reading the definition, you can use the arrow buttons to page through other definitions in the Glossary, or else press the Exit button to return to your lesson.

Don't feel obligated to click on a hotword if you already know its definition. Use them only as often as you like. If you need a definition for a term that isn't a hotword on the frame you're looking at (or doesn't appear in that frame at all) press the Glossary button after pressing the oval button to access the Glossary. To look up a term that begins with the letter "E," for example, click on the "E" on the alphabet bar on the left side of the Glossary Screen. Then use the Forward (right arrow) button to quickly page through to the definition you need.

12. Pop Quiz buttons. In most lesson, inGenious has a Pop Quiz button every few screens. The Pop Quiz Buttons like this:

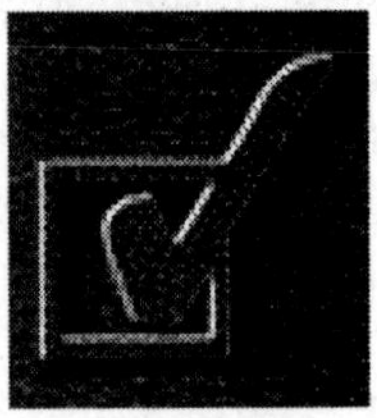

Click on the Pop Quiz button to try a sample exam question, which will give you an idea of how the material is likely to be tested on the state license exam. When you've chosen an answer, click the gold button to the left of your choice. If you've chosen the wrong answer, inGenious will prompt you to try again. When you choose the right answer, inGenious congratulates you, and you can click on the OK button to see an explanation of the answer. Click on the Exit button when you're ready to resume the lesson.

You can skip the Pop Quiz Questions if you want to, but you'll probably find that they help you understand and remember the material.

13. Games. From time to time in each lesson, you'll come across a game that will test your understanding of the material. To play the game, follow the instructions that appear on the screen.

14. Workbook Exercises. When you reach the end of a topic within a lesson, there is a summary, followed by a screen directing you to complete an exercise set in your workbook. It is not necessary to exit the program before doing the exercise set. When you're finished, return to the computer and go on to the next section of the lesson.

After you've completed all of the workbook exercises, please be sure to sign the Affidavit that follows this section. The Affidavit should also be signed by a representative of your school.

15. Lesson Quizzes. At the end of each lesson, you are required to take a quiz. The quiz questions appear in your workbook. When you have decided on your answers, enter them on the answer sheet on the computer screen, using the mouse to click on the gold button next to your answer choice. If you change your mind, simply click on a different button to change your answer. After entering all of your answers, click on the Grade Quiz button. (If you don't answer a particular question, that will be counted as an incorrect answer.) Your score will be logged as part of your student record.

16. Final Exam. When you have logged at least 60 clock hours of inGenious, you are eligible to take the final exam. Log in and then select the Final button on the Lesson Menu screen. The final consists of 220 multiple choice questions. You must score at least 70% to pass the final exam and earn your course certificate, so that you can go on to take the state license examination.

If you don't pass your first final, you can review the material and then take another exam. Even if you pass on your first attempt, feel free to take the other final exam as part of your preparation for the state license examination. Your permanent score will be the higher of the two.

17. Getting credit for the course. You must complete all 23 of the lessons and spend at least 60 hours on this course in order to take the final and obtain your course certificate. So inGenious monitors your progress and records the amount of time you spend on each lesson. Here are some things you should know about the system, to make sure that you get credit:

- If your interaction with the computer stops for more than five minutes, inGenious will stop crediting you with attendance until you resume. You can't just turn the computer on, enter a lesson, and then walk away.
- To get credit for the time you have spent on a lesson, be sure to use the Exit button to leave the program (whether you're in the middle of the lesson or at the end). When you press the Exit button, inGenious records your time and how far you got in the lesson. When you return to a lesson you didn't complete, inGenious will ask if you would like to resume where you left off, or start back at the beginning of the lesson.
- InGenious will not give you more than four hours of credit for any one lesson. (Some lessons will take less than three hours.) You may find it useful to repeat a lesson as part of your preparation for the state license examination. Just remember that there's no clock hour credit after you reach the four hour mark.
- The Pop Quiz questions, Lesson Quizzes, and the final exams are excellent study tools that will help you prepare for the state exam. Use all of them, and your chance of passing on the first attempt will soar.

Affidavit

____

Name of Student

The undersigned certify that the student named above is the individual who completed the exercises in this workbook.

____

Signature of Student

____

Signature of School Representative

Lesson 1

Real Estate as a Career

Exercise 1A

1. A person who is licensed to represent buyers and sellers in real estate transactions and to receive compensation for such services is called ______________ ______________________.

2. Which of the following types of real estate agents may work directly for a seller or buyer? (Circle all that apply.)

   a. real estate broker

   b. real estate associate broker

   c. real estate salesperson

3. In most real estate transactions, the broker's compensation takes the form of ________________________, which is usually calculated as __________________ ___________________________________.

4. Indicate whether each of the following statements is true or false.

   A broker may represent a buyer in a real estate transaction. T F

   The term "real estate agent" means the same thing as "real estate broker". T F

   Any licensed real estate agent who works on a transaction is entitled to collect a commission from the seller if the sale closes. T F

5. When a seller hires a real estate agent to help sell a home, it is called ____.

Exercise 1B

1. Real estate transactions involve a wide range of complex issues. List three types of specialists that a real estate agent may need to consult with or refer clients to.

   1. ______________________
   2. ______________________
   3. ______________________

2. Indicate whether each of the following statements is true or false.

   Real estate agents should be prepared to provide legal advice to their clients in matters regarding title to property. T F

   Buyers often rely on real estate agents to help them find suitable financing for a purchase. T F

   One of the most important services a real estate agent can offer a seller is helping to set a realistic asking price for the property. T F

3. In most cases, the single most important advantage that an agent can offer a home seller is ______________________.

4. List three reasons why sellers use real estate agents.

   1. ______________________
   2. ______________________
   3. ______________________

5. What is the disadvange to a seller if the listing price of her property is too high?

   ____

   Too low? ______________________

Exercise 1C

1. The majority of real estate agents work with ____________ property, which means they deal with the __________ and selling of homes.

2. Real estate agents provide a variety of services to buyers and sellers. Place each of the following services in the appropriate column(s) to indicate whether it benefits the seller, the buyer, or both.

   a. prepare home for showing
   b. access to multiple listing service
   c. negotiate terms of sale
   d. present offers to purchase
   e. help with the closing process
   f. help set the listing price
   g. provide expert advice

BENEFITS SELLER	BENEFITS BUYER

3. Indicate whether each of the following statements is true or false.

   A buyer's agent is always paid by the buyer. T F

   The services of a real estate agent are especially valuable to a buyer who is moving to an area that is far from the buyer's present home. T F

   Although a real estate agent may provide services to a buyer, the agent always represents only the seller; the agent never represents the buyer. T F

4. James is a first-time homebuyer and does not have much experience with real estate. Which of the following statement(s) is/are true? (Circle all that apply.)

   a. James can rely on the listing agent (who represents the seller) to help him negotiate the best deal with the seller
   b. James should consider working with his own agent as he seeks a new home
   c. A listing agent can help James locate suitable properties, prepare and present offers, arrange for financing, and deal with the details of closing the transaction

Exercise 1D

1. Which of the following agents would be entitled to payment of a commission from the seller? (Circle all that apply.)
   a. listing salesperson
   b. listing broker
   c. selling salesperson
   d. selling broker

2. Why does it matter whether an agent is classified as an employee or an independent contractor?

   ____

3. The IRS will consider a licensed real estate salesperson to be an independent contractor for federal tax purposes if two conditions are met:
   1. ____
   2. ____

4. A property sold for $100,000. In the listing agreement, the seller agreed to pay a commission of 6% of the sales price. If there is a 50/50 commission split between the listing broker and the selling broker, how much will the selling broker receive?

   ____

   If the listing broker splits her share of the commission 50/50 with the listing salesperson, how much will the salesperson receive? ____________

5. Indicate whether each of the following statements is true or false.

   If a salesperson works as an independent contractor, then the broker is not responsible for supervising the salesperson's activities. T F

   A selling broker may be a cooperating broker from a multiple listing service, or a buyer's agent. T F

   The listing broker is usually considered an employee of the seller. T F

Exercise 1E

1. Two national economic factors that have a significant effect on the housing market are ______________________ and ______________________________.

2. Why is financial security important to the success of a real estate agent's career?

   ____

3. A real estate agent must be independent and self-motivated because ________

   ____.

4. Explain how a high rate of inflation can both help and hurt a real estate career.

   ____

   ____

5. Indicate whether each of the following statements is true or false.

   Once an agent gets to know his market niche, additional training and education is of little value in helping the agent's career. T F

   Real estate is a good career for people who want to make a lot of money without doing much work. T F

   Real estate agents must enjoy working with people, and it is especially important that they be good active listeners. T F

   A real estate agent must be able to handle rejection on a regular basis. T F

Exercise 1F

1. Real estate companies differ in terms of the services they provide to ______________, and also the services they provide to ________________.

2. In choosing a real estate firm, an agent should be concerned with the company's policies in regard to:

   1. ______________________________
   2. ______________________________
   3. ______________________________
   4. ______________________________
   5. ______________________________

3. Indicate whether each of the following statements is true or false.

   Buyers and sellers always prefer to work with a real estate company that specializes in the type of property they are buying or selling. T F

   Real estate brokers are prohibited by law from engaging in dual agency. T F

   Franchise brokerages always offer more services to their agents. T F

   Most real estate companies cover their agents' business expenses for such items as travel and long distance phone charges. T F

4. List three ways in which real estate companies commonly distinguish themselves in the marketplace.

   1. ______________________________
   2. ______________________________
   3. ______________________________

5. As a rule, an agent's share of the commission split with his or her broker will be larger at a firm that provides (more / fewer) services to its agents.

Exercise 1G

1. List three different types of investment properties.

   1. ______________________________
   2. ______________________________
   3. ______________________________

3. The most popular type of commercial investment property is ______________ ______________.

4. Indicate whether each of the following statements is true or false.

   Real estate agents can represent landlords and tenants in lease transactions. T F

   An agent who specializes in residential property is less likely to be successful than an agent who specializes in commercial property. T F

   Specializing in a niche market is an effective way to build a reputation for expertise. T F

5. What is the main reason that agents want to list property?

   ____

Exercise 1H

1. There are several different types of property managers. List the distinguishing characteristics of each of the following:

   a. resident manager ______________

   b. property supervisor ______________

   c. regional manager ______________

2. Which of the following types of properties present opportunities for real estate agents who specialize in property management. (Circle all that apply.)

   a. residential

   b. commercial

   c. industrial

3. List three potential career opportunities for a real estate agent.

   1. ______________
   2. ______________
   3. ______________

Exercise 1I

1. Although real estate provides many varied career opportunities, the majority of real estate agents are engaged in ____.

2. Indicate whether each of the following statements is true or false.

   Real estate agents must be certified to act as an escrow agent for transactions in which they are not acting as the real estate agent. T F

   Washington requires all home inspectors to be licensed through the Department of Licensing. T F

   Any competent real estate agent has the requisite expertise to act as a real estate investment counselor. T F

   Membership in a trade association provides an excellent way to network with agents from other real estate companies. T F

3. Match the following terms:

___ real estate brokerage	a. closing the sale
___ property management	b. valuation of real estate
___ appraisal	c. tenant relations
___ investment counseling	d. subdivision
___ escrow	e. buyers and sellers
___ title insurance	f. title examination
___ land development	g. income property evaluation
___ home inspection	h. pre-license courses
___ real estate education	i. structural condition of property

Lesson 1J

1. The two fundamental functions of licensing laws are:
   1. ______________________________
   2. ______________________________

2. The agency responsible for administering the real estate license law in Washington is ______________________________.

3. List four possible consequences of a violation of the real estate license law.
   1. ____________________
   2. ____________________
   3. ____________________
   4. ____________________

4. The real estate recovery fund provides a source of payment for persons who are harmed by actions of real estate licensees. When a judgment is paid out of the recovery fund, what is the effect on the licensee who is involved?

   ____

   ____

5. List three types of government agencies whose regulations may affect the conduct of a real estate agent.
   1. ______________________________
   2. ______________________________
   3. ______________________________

6. The largest professional association for real estate agents is the ______________ ______________________________. Its affiliated organization in Washington is the ______________________________.

7. How many people make up the Washington Real Estate Commission? __________

8. List five qualifications for a successful real estate career.

   1. ____________________

   2. ____________________

   3. ____________________

   4. ____________________

   5. ____________________

Lesson 1: Workbook Quiz Questions

1. The term "real estate agent" refers to:
   a. a real estate broker
   b. a real estate salesperson
   c. Both of the above
   d. Neither of the above

2. Most real estate agents work exclusively with:
   a. commercial property
   b. commercial investors
   c. residential sellers
   d. residential property

3. A real estate agent needs to be well informed about all of the following subjects, except:
   a. trends in population growth
   b. financing programs
   c. schools in the local area
   d. No exceptions; an agent should be well informed about all these subjects

4. The ability of a real estate agent to help negotiate a sale can be a valuable service to:
   a. the seller
   b. the buyer
   c. Both of the above
   d. Neither of the above

5. An organization of real estate agents who share information about their listings is called:
   a. a listing cooperative
   b. a multiple listing service
   c. a board of Realtors
   d. a cartel

6. The fundamental reason that buyers and sellers use real estate agents is:
   a. they want to work with someone who is an expert in real estate transactions
   b. they want to get the best deal possible on their transaction
   c. the law requires that an agent be involved in the transaction
   d. to help guide them through the closing process

7. All of the following are important reasons for a buyer to use a real estate agent, except:
   a. real estate agents have access to all the homes listed through the MLS
   b. real estate agents can help the buyer negotiate a reasonable purchase price
   c. real estate agents are experts at preparing homes for showing
   d. real estate agents can help the buyer prepare the paperwork for the purchase

8. The most common form of compensation for a real estate agent is:
   a. a salary
   b. wages plus a bonus
   c. a commission
   d. a flat fee

9. When a salesperson works as an independent contractor, it means:
   a. the salesperson has his or her own office, and deals directly with buyers and sellers
   b. the salesperson has an associate broker's license
   c. the salesperson is not accountable to his or her broker
   d. None of the above

10. Whether or not a salesperson is an independent contractor may depend on:
    a. the degree of control exercised by the broker over the salesperson's activities
    b. the manner in which the salesperson is compensated
    c. the terms of the written employment agreement between the salesperson and the broker
    d. All of the above

11. The majority of real estate salespersons work as:
    a. employees of their brokers
    b. employees of the seller
    c. independent contractors of their brokers
    d. independent contractors of the seller

12. New real estate agents need to be financially secure because:
    a. they only receive a small fraction of the commission split
    b. a real estate agent is usually not paid until the transaction closes
    c. they need to be able to post a bond in order to be licensed
    d. All of the above

13. To be successful, a real estate agent must:
    a. be prepared to work evenings and weekends
    b. have a college degree in real estate
    c. work at least 60 hours per week
    d. operate his or her own brokerage

14. Which of the following is not a qualification for a successful real estate career?
    a. Emotional toughness
    b. Trustworthiness
    c. Education and training
    d. Overbearing personality

15. The effect of inflation on the real estate market can be to:
    a. price buyers out of the market as interest rates and home prices increase
    b. spur buyers to purchase before prices rise even more
    c. Both of the above
    d. Neither of the above

16. Commercial property is also known as:
    a. investment property
    b. non-residential property
    c. income-producing property
    d. tax-shelter property

17. Many real estate companies offer ancillary services to their clients, such as:
    a. property management
    b. escrow services
    c. investment consulting
    d. All of the above

18. The rate of commission split offered by a broker to his or her salespeople is most commonly related to:
    a. the level of services provided by the broker to the salespeople
    b. the number of salespeople in the broker's office
    c. whether the broker works primarily as a seller agent or a buyer agent
    d. whether or not the broker is a member of the local multiple listing service

19. Which of the following is not an advantage of working for a franchise real estate brokerage?
    a. Franchises have wider name recognition among the public
    b. Franchises offer greater opportunities for beginning real estate agents
    c. Franchises can participate in regional or national advertising programs
    d. Franchises often offer a variety of educational programs to their members

20. The term "real estate brokerage" refers to:
    a. the business of bringing real estate buyers and sellers together and negotiating their sales agreements
    b. the business of representing real estate sellers under the terms of listing agreements
    c. the business of buying and selling real estate for profit
    d. any business activity that relates to real estate, including property management, appraisal, escrow services and investment counseling

21. In Washington, the process of closing a real estate sale is most commonly handled by:
    a. an attorney
    b. a real estate broker
    c. an escrow agent
    d. the lender who provides the buyer's loan

22. It is increasingly common for real estate buyers to make offers conditional on an inspection of the property by a professional home inspector. The purpose of such inspections may be to:
    a. evaluate the structural soundness of the home
    b. check for termites or other pest infestations
    c. assess the quality of water and sewage treatment facilities
    d. All of the above

23. The function of real estate license laws is to:
    a. insure that real estate agents have the minimum qualifications to perform their services
    b. regulate the day-to-day business activities of real estate agents
    c. raise money for the State through license fees and penalties
    d. Both a) and b)

24. In Washington, the agency that administers the real estate license law is the:
    a. Real Estate Board
    b. Real Estate Commission
    c. Department of Real Estate
    d. Department of Licensing

25. A system of moral principles and rules that sets the standards of conduct for members of a profession is called:
    a. an oath of integrity
    b. a code of ethics
    c. a code of principles
    d. a code of responsibility

Lesson 2

The Nature of Real Property and Estates in Land

Exercise 2A

1. Real property is the land, everything attached to the land, and everything that is _______________ to the land.

2. Personal property, or personalty, is also called _____________.

3. Ownership rights are sometimes referred to as the ___________ of ___________.

4. The idea that you own the land to the center of the earth and to the upper reaches of the sky refers to which of the following? (Circle one.)

   a. Inverted pyramid

   b. Mineral rights

   c. Chattels

Exercise 2B

1. Mineral rights are considered the owner's (circle one):

   a. personal property

   b. real property

2. The legal rule which holds that the landowner who brings oil and gas to the surface may keep it all is called the rule of ___________.

3. Water rights are ________________ the land (select one):
   a. separate from
   b. appurtenant to
   c. beneath

4. True or false? Almost all water in Washington is privately owned. T F

5. Water moving in a river or stream is called _______________ water.

6. Water in a pond or a lake is called _______________ water.

7. If your land does not border a body of water, you might be able to acquire water rights by obtaining an ______________________________.

8. A property owner has a right to the natural support of his or her land. Underlying support is called (circle one):
   a. lateral support
   b. subjacent support

9. A local ordinance that might limit a property owner's use of the airspace above his or her property would be a ___________ law.

Exercise 2C

1. Trees, crops, and other plants are examples of ___________ attachments.

2. A tenant's right to harvest his or her crop after the lease has been terminated is assured by the ___________ of _______________.

3. A fixture is a (circle one):
   a. manmade attachment
   b. natural attachment
   c. covered attachment

4. All fixtures were once ____________________.

5. Once harvested from the land, trees become ________________.

6. As a general rule, real property is ______________ and personal property is ________________.

7. When a stand of timber has been sold to a lumber company, it has been ____ from the land.

Exercise 2D

1. Items used to carry on a business and not considered part of the real property, no matter how they are attached, are called ________________________.

2. A tenant installs shelving in a store he has leased for three years. It is considered (circle one):
   a. the landlord's real property
   b. the tenant's personal property

3. The five tests used to distinguish real from personal property are:
   1. ____
   2. ____
   3. ____
   4. ____
   5. ____

4. Which of the following items would ordinarily be considered real property? (Circle all that apply.)
   a. the keys to a house
   b. pews in a church
   c. a garden hose
   d. a portable dishwasher
   e. a rose bush growing in the garden
   f. a rose bush growing in a pot
   g. custom window blinds
   h. trade fixtures
   i. emblements
   j. furniture

Exercise 2E

1. A manufactured home is personal property until ______________________________ ______________________________.

2. If a manufactured home is personal property, a real estate license (is / is not) required for a dealer who sells the home.

3. Indicate whether each of the following statements is true or false.

   If a manufactured home is personal property, its sale is subject to sales tax. T F

   If a manufactured home is personal property, its sale is subject to the real estate excise tax. T F

   Most lenders will not finance the purchase of manufactured homes. T F

   The property tax rate for manufactured homes is less than the rate for site-built homes. T F

4. List three reasons why the distinction between real property and personal property is important.
   1. ______________________________
   2. ______________________________
   3. ______________________________

Exercise 2F

1. The right to possess and have exclusive use of real property is called a/an ________________.

2. The two categories of estates are:
   1. ______________________________
   2. ______________________________

3. The most extensive interest one can have in land is (circle one):
   a. fee simple conditional
   b. life estate
   c. fee simple absolute

4. When a deed stipulates that someone can have the estate until some event or act occurs, it creates a ______________________ estate.

5. List two types of freehold estates.
   1. ______________________________
   2. ______________________________

6. Most freehold estates are ______________________________ estates.

7. The life upon which a life estate depends is called the ______________________________.

8. The person who has the title during the life estate is the (circle one):
   a. grantor
   b. life tenant
   c. remainderman

9. If a property owner deeds the title to her property to Jones on the condition that it will return to the owner on Jones's death, what do we call the owner's interest? (Circle one.)
   a. An estate in remainder
   b. An estate in reversion
   c. A fee simple estate

10. Smith deeds to Abernathy for the life of Jones. On the death of Jones title shall pass to Adams.

    Smith is the ______________________.

    Abernathy is the ____________________.

    Jones is the ______________________.

    Adams is the ______________________.

11. A life tenant must not commit ___________, meaning that he or she must not injure, alter, or destroy the premises.

Exercise 2G

1. A less-than-freehold estate is more commonly called a ____________________ estate.

2. A leasehold estate is created by a contract called a __________________.

3. Another name for the landlord is ___________, and the tenant is also called a ___________.

4. Match the terms on the left with the appropriate descriptions on the right.

___ Estate for years	a. Indefinite period of time; can be terminated at any time by either party
___ Periodic estate	b. Definite period of time; terminates automatically
___ Estate at will	c. Tenant holds over against landlord's will
___ Tenancy at sufferance	d. Continues for successive similar periods until terminated with proper notice

5. The term "surrender" refers to:
   a. termination of a lease by mutual agreement
   b. a consequence of eviction

6. An arrangement in which a new tenant agrees to take over the original tenant's lease payments for the remainder of the term is called ______________________.

Exercise 2H

1. Circle the correct statement(s) below.
   a. A lease is not a type of contract
   b. Both landlord and tenant must sign the lease
   c. The landlord's signature must be notarized if the lease's term exceeds one year

2. The type of lease that must be in writing, regardless of its duration, is the ___________________________.

3. Which of the following must every valid lease include? (Circle all that are correct.)
   a. Tenant's signature
   b. Property description
   c. Notary's seal

4. Which of the following would NOT represent a limitation on a tenant's use of the property? (Circle one.)
   a. Zoning
   b. Escalation clause
   c. Private restrictions
   d. Lease terms

5. A tenant's security deposit can be used for unpaid rent, cleaning, and unusual damage caused by the tenant. It cannot be used to correct damage caused by reasonable __________ and __________.

6. That portion of the security deposit that the tenant is entitled to must be returned by the landlord within ________ days after the termination of the tenancy.

Exercise 2I

1. An assignee in connection with a lease assumes:

   ___ primary

   ___ secondary

   ___ no

   responsibility for the rent payments.

2. Match the term on the left to the appropriate description on the right.

___ Assignment	a.	Original tenant transfers possession to new tenant for part of remaining lease term
___ Sublease	b.	Yielding or giving up a leasehold estate before its expiration
___ Surrender	c.	Transfer by tenant for the entire balance of unexpired lease term
___ Novation	d.	Original lease agreement is replaced by a new one

3. If an owner sells property that is subject to a lease, is the buyer obligated to honor the existing lease agreement? _____

Exercise 2J

1. List seven ways in which a lease may terminate before the end of the term.
   1. ______________________________
   2. ______________________________
   3. ______________________________
   4. ______________________________
   5. ______________________________
   6. ______________________________
   7. ______________________________

2. The covenant of ____________________ is breached if the tenant is wrongfully evicted.

3. ________________ eviction occurs if the landlord orders the tenant to leave the property, or physically forces the tenant out.

4. ________________ eviction occurs if the landlord allows a substantial interference with the tenant's possession of the property.

5. What creates an ongoing duty to maintain the property in a livable condition? (Circle one.)
   a. Warranty of habitability
   b. Covenant of quiet enjoyment

6. If a tenant fails to pay rent according to the terms of the lease agreement, the landlord must give proper notice before filing an __________________________ action.

7. Match the term on the left to its definition on the right.

___ Writ of possession	a.	A legal action to regain possession of real property
___ Covenant of quiet enjoyment	b.	Implied assurance that property meets with all housing code regulations pertaining to safety and sanitation
___ Unlawful detainer action	c.	Promise that tenant's possession of leased property will not be disturbed
___ Warranty of habitability	d.	Court order requiring tenant to vacate premises

8. Condemnation of leased property ______________ the lease.

Exercise 2K

1. Match the term on the left to its description on the right.

___ Gross lease	a.	Fixed rent paid during specified period, but rent is increased a certain intervals
___ Graduated lease	b.	Corporation owns the building but is only leasing the land
___ Percentage lease	c.	Fixed rent paid by tenant; landlord pays operating expenses
___ Net lease	d.	Tenant pays base rent plus a proportionate share of property taxes, insurance, and maintenance
___ Ground lease	e.	Tenant pays base rent plus a share of its gross or net earnings

2. The type of lease most often used for residential rentals is the ______________ __________.

3. A percentage lease would most likely be used when the tenant is a ______________ ______________.

4. "Index lease" is another name for a ____.

Lesson 2: Workbook Quiz Questions

1. Real property includes:
   a. anything appurtenant to the land
   b. anything severed from the land
   c. chattels
   d. personalty

2. The distinction between real property and personal property is important in a real estate sale because:
   a. the legal description depends on this distinction
   b. anything that is part of the real property is transferred to the buyer, unless otherwise agreed
   c. the buyer is only responsible for the cost of the real property
   d. only realty may be transferred in a purchase and sale agreement

3. The "bundle of rights" does not include the right to:
   a. lease to a tenant
   b. do nothing
   c. impede air traffic
   d. mortgage the property

4. Personal property is:
   a. chattels
   b. personalty
   c. usually movable
   d. All of the above

5. Air rights, mineral rights, and water rights are all:
   a. attachments
   b. freehold estates
   c. leasehold rights
   d. appurtenances

6. Condominium developments are made possible by:
   a. air rights
   b. water rights
   c. constructive severance
   d. leasehold estates

7. Once coal has been extracted from the earth, it is:
   a. personal property
   b. an attachment
   c. a mineral right
   d. real property

8. The rule that allows a property owner to remove natural gas that lies under the property of another is the rule of:
   a. littoral rights
   b. capture
   c. appropriation
   d. lateral support

9. A pond wholly within the boundaries of a piece of private property in the state of Washington is:
   a. owned by the state
   b. subject to state permit requirements before the owner can use the water
   c. privately owned water
   d. appropriated water

10. A stream borders both Peter's and Patty's land. Which of the following correctly describes Peter and Patty's rights?
    a. They can both use the stream only if it is navigable
    b. The upstream landowner has priority in regard to water use
    c. Neither one can use the water without a permit
    d. Both owners have equal rights to use the water

11. In Washington a landowner whose land does not border a body of water:
    a. may be granted an appropriation permit
    b. may use water from the nearest available source
    c. is a littoral owner
    d. may divert water from riparian land

12. Support from adjacent land is called:
    a. lateral support
    b. littoral rights
    c. subjacent support
    d. constructive support

13. Growing trees that have not been sold are:
    a. riparian crops
    b. natural attachments
    c. fixtures
    d. personal property

14 An interest in land is called an "estate" if it:
    a. is or may become possessory
    b. cannot be inherited
    c. is owned in severalty
    d. does not include title

15. An estate is either:
    a. a joint tenancy or a periodic tenancy
    b. a freehold or a leasehold
    c. a tenancy in common or a joint venture
    d. a fee simple determinable or an estate of inheritance

16. The highest and most complete form of ownership, representing the whole "bundle of rights," is called:
    a. a qualified fee
    b. an estate for years
    c. a fee simple absolute
    d. an estate in reversion

17. When a fee simple owner transfers title by deed, it is presumed that the new owner (the grantee) receives:
    a. an estate for years
    b. an estate in remainder
    c. a joint tenancy
    d. a fee simple absolute

18. A freehold estate whose duration is limited to the lifetime of a specified person is called:
    a. a fee simple subject to a condition subsequent
    b. an estate for years
    c. an estate of inheritance
    d. a life estate

19. If A grants a parcel of property to B for the life of C, then:
    a. B is the life tenant and C's life is the measuring life
    b. A is the life tenant and B has an estate in remainder
    c. C is the life tenant and A's life is the measuring life
    d. C is the life tenant and A has an estate in remainder

20. A leasehold estate:
    a. gives the tenant the right of exclusive possession
    b. has an indeterminable duration
    c. is a nonpossessory interest
    d. is an estate in reversion

21. A tenancy for a fixed term is called:
    a. an estate at will
    b. an estate for years
    c. a periodic estate
    d. a tenancy in common

22. Termination of a lease by mutual consent is called:
    a. reversion
    b. sufferance
    c. surrender
    d. waste

23. At the end of the period, a periodic tenancy automatically:

    a. terminates and cannot be renewed
    b. terminates unless one of the parties gives proper notice of renewal
    c. renews itself unless both parties agree to terminate it
    d. renews itself unless one of the parties gives proper notice of termination

24. If a tenant who came into possession under a valid lease holds over without the landlord's permission after the lease has expired, it's called:

    a. a tenancy at sufferance
    b. an estate at will
    c. a tenancy in waste
    d. a freehold estate

25. Like an estate for years, a periodic tenancy:

    a. is assignable unless assignment is prohibited by the terms of the lease agreement
    b. must be surrendered upon proper notice
    c. must last at least one year
    d. automatically expires upon the death of the landlord

Lesson 3

Methods of Holding Title and Encumbrances on Land

Exercise 3A

1. The one type of ownership that is not concurrent is ownership in ________________.

2. What type of concurrent ownership carries with it the right of survivorship?

   ____

3. One of the forms of concurrent ownership requires four unities. What is it called?

   ____

   Name the four unities:

   1. ________________
   2. ________________
   3. ________________
   4. ________________

4. Perkins and Dole own property as joint tenants. Dole sells her interest to Russell. Perkins and Russell own the property as ____________________________________.

Exercise 3B

1. Name the four types of concurrent ownership discussed in this lesson.
   1. ______________________
   2. ______________________
   3. ______________________
   4. ______________________

2. Match the type of ownership listed on the left with the phrase on the right most closely associated with it.

___ Joint tenancy	a.	Only one unity required
___ Community property	b.	One owner
___ Severalty	c.	Cannot be devised
___ Tenancy in common	d.	Marriage

3. Smith deeds 10 of her interest in a parcel of land to her cousin Casey. What type of ownership do they have? (Circle one.)
   a. Joint tenancy
   b. Tenancy in common
   c. Community property
   d. Tenancy in severalty

4. Miller and Callahan own a property together. When Miller dies, his creditors cannot attach the property. What kind of ownership existed between Miller and Callahan?

   ____

5. Community property is defined as everything owned by a married couple that is not ______________________.

Exercise 3C

1. Match term on the left to the corresponding term or definition on the right.

___ General partnership	a.	One project only
___ REIT	b.	Participation in management prohibited
___ Joint venture	c.	Ongoing business; unlimited liability
___ Limited partnership	d.	Minimum 100 owners
___ Corporation	e.	Perpetual existence

2. One kind of partnership agreement is required to be in writing.. Which one is it? (Circle one.)
   a. General partnership agreement
   b. Limited partnership agreement

3. What is regarded by the law as a single, separate, artificial person?

   ___________________________.

4. In a corporation, the ____________________elect the __________________ _______________, which supervises the _______________, who manage the day-to-day corporate business.

5. The term limited liability does not apply to one of the individuals below. Which one?
   a. Corporate stockholder
   b. General partner
   c. REIT investor
   d. Limited partner

Exercise 3D

1. A condominium owner holds title to his or her unit _______________________, and owns a share of the project's common areas as a _________________________.

2. Indicate whether each of the following statements is true or false.

   The owner of a condominium receives a deed to his or her unit. T F

   Each unit in a condominium project is subject to a blanket mortgage. T F

   If a lien against a condominium unit is foreclosed, the other units in the project are not affected. T F

   Sale of a condominium unit usually requires approval of the other owners in the project. T F

3. In most cases, transfer of a unit in a cooperative is subject to the approval of the members of the cooperative. Why is it important for a cooperative to exercise control over who is allowed to buy an interest in one of its units?

   ____

   ____

4. Indicate whether each of the following statements is true or false.

   The primary difference between a condominium and a cooperative is the method of sharing title to common areas. T F

   Each unit in a cooperative receives a separate property tax assessment. T F

   A person who buys a cooperative unit is really buying shares in a corportation, along with the right to lease the cooperative unit. T F

5. The cooperative form of ownership is most accurately described as:

   a. ownership in severalty

   b. a joint tenancy

   c. a tenancy in common

Exercise 3E

1. An encumbrance is a (possessory / nonpossessory) interest in property.

2. A lien is a creditor's ____________________ interest in the debtor's property.

3. Circle the statements that apply to a secured creditor:
   a. must sue to force payment of debt
   b. is a lienholder
   c. can only hold security interest in real property
   d. is better off than unsecured creditor

4. A mortgage lien is a (voluntary / involuntary) lien. It is an example of a (general / specific) lien.

5. A general lien attaches to __________ of a debtor's property.

Exercise 3F

1. Mark each type of lien listed below with the appropriate letters to indicate whether it is voluntary or involuntary, and general or specific.

   v=voluntary; i=involuntary   g=general; s=specific

   a. _____ construction lien
   b. _____ judgment lien
   c. _____ mortgage lien
   d. _____ property tax lien
   e. _____ IRS lien
   f. _____ deed of trust lien

2. In a deed of trust, the borrower is called the ____________________ or ____________________, and the lender is called the ____________________.

3. The main difference between a mortgage and a deed of trust is in the methods of ____________________.

4. Another name for a construction lien is ____________________ lien.

5. The party in a lawsuit found to owe money to another party is the ____________________ debtor.

Exercise 3G

1. When a property has more than one lien against it, the lienholder to be paid first has first lien ________________.

2. The rule "First to record, first in right," refers to the general rule that lien priority is set by date of ________________.

3. In Washington, two types of liens have priority over all others, regardless of recording date. These are:______________________________ and ______________________________.

4. Priority of a construction lien is determined by the date ________________ ______________ begins.

Exercise 3H

1. True or false? Washington's homestead law protects the land and outbuildings, in addition to the dwelling itself. T F

2. Homestead protection (circle all that apply):
   a. requires a recorded Declaration of Homestead
   b. prohibits foreclosure on a deed of trust
   c. extends to the net equity or $30,000, whichever is less
   d. provides some protection against judgment creditors
   e. does not cover liens resulting from nonpayment of child support
   f. extends to the proceeds from the recent sale of a homestead

3. Homestead protection is automatically terminated if the owner fails to occupy the property for a period of ________________, unless the owner files a ____________ ________________________________.

Exercise 3I

1. Match each term with the correct description:

___ easement in gross		a.	runs with the dominant tenement
___ dominant tenant		b.	parcel of land with the burden
___ easement appurtenant		c.	commercial easement
___ servient tenement		d.	owner of the benefited land
___ a type of easement in gross that can be assigned		e.	a personal right

2. An easement holder has a right to ___________ the property of another, but does not have the right of ____.

3. Nelson owns no property, but he has an easement that allows him to use Betty's track to exercise his horses. He has an easement ____________________.

4. True or false? An easement is a nonpossessory interest that burdens the landowner's title. T F

Exercise 3J

1. Match the methods of creating an easement with the appropriate descriptions:

___ express grant	a.	Marco sells waterfront property adjacent to his house, reserving an easement across the property so that he can launch his boat
___ express reservation	b.	Barbara refuses to grant an easement to the county to build a public trail over her land, so the county acts unilaterally to create an easement
___ implication	c.	An easement created by long-term use without the owner's permission, acquired in a manner similar to that of acquiring title by adverse possession
___ prescription	d.	Erik has given Abe written permission to use the private road across Erik's property as a shortcut to the county highway
___ condemnation	e.	The easement created when Marsha sells half of her property and neglects to include a reservation of easement for access to the remaining half of the property

2. An easement created by express grant must be in writing and signed by the ________________.

3. The requirements for an easement created by implication are:
   1. it must be ______________________________ for the enjoyment of the dominant tenement, and
   2. there must have been apparent ________________.

4. A prescriptive easement can be created even without ______________________, which is a requirement for acquiring title by adverse possession.

5. True or false? Because a grant of easement does not transfer title, it does not need to be recorded. T F

Exercise 3K

1. Match the terms with the event that will result in that type of termination:

___ release	a. the cessation of the purpose for which the easement was established
___ merger	b. acquisition of the servient tenement by the holder of the easement
___ failure of purpose	c. the dominant tenant gives up rights in the servient tenement
___ abandonment	d. acts of the easement holder that indicate an intent to abandon the easement
___ prescription	e. servient tenant prevents dominant tenant from using the easement for the period required by statute

2. Non-use of an easement for a prolonged period of time (is / is not) generally considered equivalent to abandonment.

3. Acquiring an easement by prescription is comparable to acquiring title by ______________________________.

4. Francois has an access easement across Madelaine's property, but doesn't use it very often because there is an alternate access to his property that is more convenient. If Madelaine builds a fence that blocks Francois' easement (circle all the options that are true):
   a. the easement is terminated by abandonment
   b. Francois will lose the right to use the easement unless he tears the fence down
   c. the easement may be terminated by prescription if Francois does not take action to have the fence removed
   d. the easement is terminated by failure of purpose
   e. the easement is terminated automatically, since Francois has an alternate access to his property

5. Bjorn and Oleg have been fishing buddies for many years, and Bjorn has given Oleg a formal easement to enter his property and fish in the stream that runs through it. If Bjorn sells the property, what happens to the easement?

____

Exercise 3L

1. Someone who has a profit is allowed to ____________________ from land belonging to someone else.

2. Private restrictions are restrictions on the use of a property that may have been imposed by (circle all that can be correct):
   a. a previous owner of the property
   b. the original developer of the property
   c. a neighboring landowner
   d. the local government
   e. the state government

3. Like easements, private restrictions ______________ with the land, which means they are binding on subsequent owners of the property.

4. How are private restrictions on the use of property enforced?

____

____

5. The most common private restrictions are those imposed by developers who set up CC&Rs for their subdivisions. Why do developers go to the trouble of establishing private restrictions for their developments?

____

____

6. When in doubt, a court will usually construe a private restriction as a _______________, rather than a _______________.

Exercise 3M

1. Match the following terms:

___ license	a. trespass
___ declaration of restrictions	b. consequence of violating a condition
___ forfeiture of title	c. CC&Rs
___ injunction	d. consequence of violating a covenant
___ encroachment	e. verbal permission to use land

2. List the following statements under the property heading shown below.
   a. Can only be granted in writing
   b. Runs with the land
   c. Can be revoked at any time
   d. May be granted orally or in writing
   e. An encumbrance
   f. Not an interest in real property
   g. Could be created by prescription

Easement	License

3. An encroachment (is / is not) an encumbrance. Encroachments (are / are not) covered by standard title insurance policies.

4. What is the difference between a financial encumbrance and a non-financial encumbrance?

   ____

5. What is the difference between an encumbrance and an estate?

   ____

6. Jean owns a house that she has rented to Mark on a one-year term lease. The house is subject to a $70,000 mortgage, and there is an easement across the property for access to an adjoining parcel. Indicate whether each of the following statements is true or false.

   If the lender forecloses the mortgage, the lease will terminate automatically. T F

   If the lender forecloses the mortgage, the easement will terminate automatically. T F

   Mark's leasehold interest is not affected by the easement. T F

   If Jean sells the property, the new owner must honor the mortgage, the lease and the easement. T F

Lesson 3: Workbook Quiz Questions

1. Property is owned in severalty when:
   a. there is a right of survivorship
   b. it is subject to a lease
   c. it is owned by several people concurrently
   d. one person is the sole owner

2. When property is held in joint tenancy, upon the death of one of the joint tenants, his or her interest in the property automatically:
   a. vests in his or her spouse
   b. is transferred to his or her heirs
   c. passes to the other joint tenant(s)
   d. becomes an estate for years

3. Tenancy in common always involves:
   a. unity of time, title, and interest
   b. unity of time and possession
   c. unity of time and title
   d. unity of possession

4. Which of the following is considered community property in Washington?
   a. Property a husband purchased before he got married
   b. Property a wife acquired by inheritance during her marriage
   c. Property a wife purchased with wages that she earned during her marriage
   d. Property a husband was given by a friend before his marriage

5. When a corporation owns property, title is held:
   a. in severalty, in the corporation's name
   b. by the shareholders, as tenants in common
   c. by the general partners, in trust
   d. by the limited partners, as community property

6. In a condominium:
   a. a corporation owns the entire complex
   b. each unit is separately owned, but the unit owners share ownership of the common areas as tenants in common
   c. all of the residents own the entire complex as joint tenants
   d. the entire complex is owned by an REIT

7. The type of lien that results from local improvements (such as road paving) which benefit a limited group of property owners is called:
   a. a special assessment lien
   b. an ad valorem lien
   c. a mechanic's lien
   d. a cost/benefit lien

8. When the proceeds of a foreclosure sale aren't enough to pay off all of the liens against the property:
   a. each lienholder receives a pro rata share of the proceeds
   b. the lien with highest priority is paid off first, even if there is no money left over for the other liens
   c. the liens automatically attach to other property owned by the debtor
   d. the sale is void

9. Lien priority is generally established by recording date, but special priority is given to:
   a. mortgages and deeds of trust
   b. general liens
   c. property tax and special assessment liens
   d. judgment liens

10. In Washington, homestead protection:
    a. is only established if the property owner records a Declaration of Homestead
    b. applies to mortgages and construction liens as well as judgment liens
    c. gives judgment liens higher priority than mortgages
    d. is automatic, beginning as soon as the owner starts living on the property

11. An easement is a type of:
    a. nonpossessory interest
    b. estate
    c. lien
    d. encroachment

12. The parcel of land that receives the benefit of an easement appurtenant is called the:
    a. dominant tenement
    b. servient tenement
    c. servient tenant
    d. parcel in gross

13. Because an easement appurtenant runs with the land, if the servient tenement is sold:
    a. the new owner still has the right to use the easement
    b. the new owner still has to let the dominant tenant use the easement
    c. the easement becomes an easement in gross
    d. the easement is extinguished by abandonment

14. A driveway easement providing access to Lot B across Lot A is:
    a. a servient easement
    b. an easement in gross
    c. an easement appurtenant
    d. an easement by merger

15. An easement in gross:
    a. is the same thing as a license
    b. can be assigned from one person to another
    c. benefits a servient tenement rather than a dominant tenement
    d. benefits a person rather than a parcel of land

16. An easement created by express grant or by express reservation:
    a. cannot run with the land
    b. must be in writing
    c. must be reasonably necessary for the enjoyment of the dominant tenement
    d. All of the above

17. When the property was divided into two lots, the grantor failed to reserve an access easement across Lot A for the benefit of Lot B. Even so, if an easement is reasonably necessary and there was apparent prior use, there is an easement by:
    a. express grant
    b. prescription
    c. dedication
    d. implication

18. An easement created through long-term use of land without the permission of the owner is an easement by:
    a. prescription
    b. merger
    c. implication
    d. reservation

19. The owner of Lot B has an access easement across Lot A. Then the owner of Lot B buys Lot A. The easement is terminated through:

    a. merger
    b. failure of purpose
    c. prescription
    d. abandonment

20. An easement can be terminated by release:

    a. only after ten years of non-use
    b. only if the purpose for which it was created ends
    c. if the servient tenant records a declaration of intent to abandon
    d. if the dominant tenant is willing to give it up

21. The difference between an easement and a profit is that a profit:

    a. can be revoked by the landowner
    b. is usually not put into writing
    c. allows something to be removed from the land
    d. is not an encumbrance

22. Private restrictions:

    a. are typically imposed by the city or county government
    b. are considered unconstitutional
    c. do not run with the land
    d. are binding on subsequent owners of the property

23. Violation of a private restriction is most likely to lead to:

    a. a mechanic's lien
    b. merger
    c. an injunction
    d. forfeiture of title

24. Verbal (unwritten) permission to cross someone else's property is:

    a. a license
    b. a profit
    c. a covenant
    d. an easement in gross

25. Which of these is an example of an encroachment?

    a. CC&Rs
    b. A toolshed built partially over the boundary on the neighbor's land
    c. Permission to pick berries on the neighbor's property
    d. All of the above

Lesson 4

Public Restrictions on Land

Exercise 4A

1. A government can exercise its police power in order to protect the public __________, __________, morals, and welfare.

2. Local governments receive their police power by delegation from the __________ government.

3. Which of the following requirements must a land use regulation meet in order for it to be constitutional?

   a. It must be a restrictive covenant.

   b. It must not reduce the property's value so much that it amounts to a confiscation of property.

   c. It must prevent the harm that would be caused by the prohibited use.

   d. It must be a zoning ordinance.

   e. It must be reasonably related to public health, safety, morals, or welfare.

   f. It must not restrict private land use.

   g. It must not be discriminatory.

4. List three examples of the government's exercise of its police power in relation to real estate.

   1. ____

   2. ____

   3. ____

Exercise 4B

1. List the four primary goals of Washington's Growth Management Act.

    1. ______________________________
    2. ______________________________
    3. ______________________________
    4. ______________________________

2. What is the function of a planning commission?

    ____

3. Indicate whether each of the following statements is true or false.

    Zoning laws are an exercise of the police power. T F

    The general plan for an area controls the type of zoning laws that may be established. T F

    Zoning laws are created by the planning commission. T F

    Zoning laws can control the height, size and shape of buildings. T F

4. What are the four basic classifications of land use for zoning purposes?

    1. ______________________________
    2. ______________________________
    3. ______________________________
    4. ______________________________

5. Under the ______________________________, building size is controlled by regulating the ratio between the area of a building's floor space and the area of the lot it occupies.

Exercise 4C

1. Match the terms to the appropriate description or example.

___ rezone	a. zoning amendment
___ variance	b. authorization to build a garage that will fail to meet setback requirements by three feet
___ nonconforming use	c. allows a new hospital to be built in a residential zone
___ conditional use	d. often arises when an area is zoned for the first time

2. True or false? If a nonconforming use is sold, the new owner must discontinue that use and comply with the zoning. T F

3. Although non-conforming uses are allowed to continue, they may not be ________________ or ______________________________.

4. List three types of uses that are commonly established under conditional use permits.

   1. ______________________________
   2. ______________________________
   3. ______________________________

5. Indicate whether each of the following statements is true or false.

   A request for a variance usually requires that a public hearing be held. T F

   An owner is more likely to be successful if she applies for a rezone rather than a variance. T F

   In most cases, a variance allows only a minor deviation from the existing zoning requirements. T F

Exercise 4D

1. Match each term with the appropriate description:

___ plat map	a. generally issued before construction begins if plans comply with building codes
___ subdivision	b. issued after construction is completed
___ building permit	c. submitted in order to obtain permission to subdivide
___ certificate of occupancy	d. division of land into two or more pieces

2. The Washington Land Development Act is a subdivision law that is also a _______________ protection law.

3. The Interstate Land Sales Full Disclosure Act is a federal consumer protection law that applies to subdivisions for sale in _______________ commerce.

4. A subdivision is exempt from the Washington Land Development Act if: (circle all that apply)
   a. it has fewer than 26 lots
   b. it is located in another state
   c. all of the lots are at least one acre in size
   d. it is located within city limits
   e. it has more than 100 lots
   f. the lots all have buildings on them

Exercise 4E

1. Match the terms with the appropriate descriptions:

___ NEPA	a. the state version of the federal environmental act
___ SEPA	b. requires an environmental impact statement for certain federal actions
___ Shoreline Management Act	c. examines the effect a proposed project will have on environmental and other factors
___ environmental impact statement	d. regulates development near water

2. The Shoreline Management Act regulates development within __________ of the high water mark. It applies to coastal shorelines, shores of lakes larger than ___________, and shores of streams flowing at a rate of more than _______ ____________________.

3. Which of the following actions are subject to the conditions of the State Environmental Policy Act? (Circle all that apply.)
   a. issuance of a building permit
   b. issuance of a variance
   c. issuance of a conditional use permit
   d. amendment of a zoning ordinance

4. True or false? Under CERCLA, a property owner may be required to pay environmental cleanup costs, even if he was not responsible for causing the contamination. T F

Exercise 4F

1. Three types of government power that affect property ownership are:
   1. ________________________________
   2. ________________________________
   3. ________________________________

2. Circle the terms in the following list that have the same meaning:
   a. general property taxes
   b. special assessments
   c. residential taxes
   d. general real estate taxes
   e. excise tax
   f. ad valorem taxes

3. The Latin phrase "ad valorem" means according to __________.

4. A valuation of property for tax purposes is an ________________.

5. Match the items in the two columns below:

___ taxes are based on value as of this date	a. annually
___ payment of first half of taxes due	b. every four years
___ physical appraisal	c. April 30
___ assessment	d. October 31
___ payment of second half of taxes due	e. January 1

6. To figure the amount of property taxes owed, multiply the assessed value by the ____________________.

7. Classify the following statements as describing a general real estate tax (g), a special assessment (s), or both (b):

    ____ creates a lien

    ____ a one-time charge

    ____ all property within taxing district is taxed

    ____ amount of taxes is based on value of property

    ____ also known as improvement tax

    ____ amount assessed is based on benefit received

8. Each sale of real property in Washington is subject to a real estate ____________ tax. This tax is the responsibility of the (buyer / seller).

Lesson 4: Workbook Quiz Questions

1. The constitutional basis for zoning and other land use control laws is:
   a. the government's police power
   b. eminent domain
   c. the Civil Rights Act of 1866
   d. the government's power to tax property on the basis of value

2. As a general rule, a zoning law will only be considered constitutional if it:
   a. does not reduce the value of the regulated property
   b. is related to the protection of the public health, safety, morals, or general welfare
   c. controls the ratio between floor area and lot size
   d. All of the above

3. The central task of a planning commission is to:
   a. enact zoning laws
   b. implement building codes
   c. design a comprehensive plan for development
   d. determine the highest and best use for each property

4. A zoning ordinance may:
   a. regulate the height of buildings
   b. have setback requirements
   c. limit a property to certain uses
   d. All of the above

5. The owners of a nonconforming use are typically prohibited from:
   a. continuing the nonconforming use when a new zoning ordinance is adopted
   b. changing their property to a use that complies with the new zoning ordinance
   c. petitioning for a rezone
   d. enlarging the nonconforming use or rebuilding it if the property is destroyed

6. A variance usually will not be granted unless the property owner:
   a. faces severe practical difficulties or undue hardship as a result of the zoning
   b. is prevented from making the most profitable use of the land because of the zoning
   c. is eligible for a conditional use permit under the current ordinance
   d. has applied for a rezone, and that request has been denied

7. A conditional use permit would be most likely to allow:
   a. a hospital to be located in a residential neighborhood
   b. a factory to emit limited quantities of air pollutants
   c. a house to be built two feet closer to the property line than the setback rules allow
   d. development of a subdivision with more than 25 lots

8. A rezone is the same thing as:
   a. a variance
   b. a zoning amendment
   c. a nonconforming use
   d. an EIS

9. Before adding a room to a house, the homeowner is usually required to obtain a:
   a. variance
   b. conditional use permit
   c. building permit
   d. certificate of occupancy

10. A developer is subdividing property into ten lots, planning to build houses on them. Before selling any of these lots to individual buyers, the developer must:
    a. issue a Public Offering Statement
    b. comply with the Interstate Land Sales Full Disclosure Act
    c. comply with the Washington Land Development Act
    d. get the plat approved by the appropriate county and/or city officials

11. The Washington Land Development Act applies when certain subdivision property is advertised for sale in this state:
    a. even if the property is located in another state
    b. only if the property is located in Washington State
    c. only if the property is located in another state
    d. only if the developer has not submitted a plat for approval in Washington

12. Which of the following is a federal law that requires an environmental impact statement to be prepared under certain circumstances?
    a. NEPA
    b. CERCLA
    c. ILSFDA
    d. SEPA

13. The government is required to pay just compensation to a property owner:
    a. if the value of the property is reduced by an exercise of the police power
    b. if the property is taken away by an exercise of the power of eminent domain
    c. only if the property is condemned for a private purpose rather than a public purpose
    d. only if the owner had a reasonable expectation of short-term profit from the property

14. General real estate taxes are sometimes called ad valorem taxes because they are:
    a. used only to pay for environmental cleanup
    b. levied annually
    c. based on the value of the property taxed
    d. based on the benefit the taxpayer receives from government services

15. General real estate taxes:
    a. do not affect title to property
    b. must be paid before title can be transferred
    c. create a lien against the taxed property only if allowed to become delinquent
    d. create a lien against the taxed property when levied

16. In Washington, a property owner is expected to pay at least the first half of the general real estate taxes by:
    a. February 15
    b. April 30
    c. July 15
    d. October 31

17. In Washington, general real estate taxes are levied against:.
    a. residential property only
    b. residential and commercial property only
    c. commercial and industrial property only
    d. all real property, unless the property is specifically exempt

18. Unlike general real estate taxes, special assessments are levied:
    a. to pay for a specific improvement
    b. every year
    c. against all taxable real property within a taxing district
    d. All of the above

19. The real estate excise tax is:
    a. calculated as a percentage of the property's selling price
    b. calculated as a percentage of the property's true and fair value
    c. collected when the property is first listed for sale
    d. collected only if the property is sold to an out-of-state buyer

20. In 1990, Washington passed a significant new land use planning law that requires new development to be concentrated in compact urban growth areas that are contiguous with presently urbanized areas. This law is called:
    a. the Comprehensive Planning Act
    b. the Environmental Protection Act
    c. the Urban Growth Act
    d. the Growth Management Act

21. Which of the following would not be considered a valid exercise of the state's police power?
    a. a building code regulation that requires minimum amounts of reinforcing steel in building foundations
    b. a zoning law that limits the maximum height of structures
    c. a law that requires all private property owners in a neighborhood to dedicate easements across their properties for a new public utility line
    d. a law that limits the use of certain properties to residential use only

22. The "floor area ratio" method:
    a. is used to regulate the size of a building in relation to the size of its lot
    b. allows for more flexibility in building design than conventional height and setback regulations
    c. is not applicable in all situations
    d. All of the above

23. A religious congregation wishes to build a house of worship in an area that is zoned for residential use. The congregation should:
    a. apply for a rezone
    b. apply for a non-conforming use permit
    c. apply for a conditional use permit
    d. apply for a variance

24. A valid subdivision plat must contain all of the following items except:

    a. a verification that the property taxes are current
    b. a legal description of the lands to be subdivided
    c. a statement of the landowner's consent to the subdivision
    d. a provision for any dedications that the county or city may require, such as dedication of land within the subdivision for public streets

25. Which of the following statements best describes the effect of the real estate excise tax?

    a. The tax must be paid by the seller, so the buyer doesn't need to worry about it
    b. The seller is required to pay the tax, but the tax will result in a lien against the buyer's property if the seller doesn't pay it
    c. The buyer is required to pay the tax, and the seller is not involved in the process at all
    d. The buyer and the seller are each responsible for paying one half of the tax

Lesson 5

Contract Law

Exercise 5A

1. Helen Kristofides offered the Vogels $26,000 for their land, and they've agreed to sell it to her. They will transfer title to her next week. This contract is (pick one from each pair):

express	implied
unilateral	bilateral
executory	executed

2. When one party has promised to pay if the other party performs as requested, but the other party has not promised to perform, it is called a ____________________ contract.

3. A contract is executory until ______________________________.

4. What is the definition of a contract?

   ____

5. Indicate whether each of the following statements is true or false.

Express contracts are always executory.	T F
In an implied contract, both parties are obligated to perform.	T F
In a unilateral contract, only one party signs the agreement.	T F

Exercise 5B

1. In Washington, to have contractual capacity, a person must be:
   1. ________________________________
   2. ________________________________

2. A contract entered into by a minor is (void / voidable).

3. A contract entered into by a person who has been declared incompetent by a court is (void / voidable).

4. A contract entered into by someone who was temporarily incompetent may be (void / voidable).

5. A __________________________ can enter into a legally binding contract on behalf of a minor or an incompetent person.

6. Mutual consent to the terms of a contract is achieved through the process of __________________________.

Exercise 5C

1. If an offer terminates before ______________________, no contract is formed.

2. Which of these terminates a contract offer? (Circle all that are correct.)
   a. Rejection by offeree
   b. Revocation by offeror
   c. Counteroffer by offeree
   d. Death of offeror

3. Joe Nash made a contract offer to Roy Sheridan. Sheridan agreed to most of the terms of the offer, but he made a few minor changes. Sheridan's response to Nash's offer is called a ____________________.

4. A contract cannot be enforced against someone who signed it (circle all that are correct):
   a. without reading it first
   b. as a result of undue influence
   c. and then changed his or her mind

5. Match the following terms.

___ actual fraud	a. taking advantage of trust
___ constructive fraud	b. intentional deception
___ undue influence	c. threat of force
___ duress	d. unintentional deception

Exercise 5D

1. List the four basic requirements for a valid contract:
   1. ______________________________
   2. ______________________________
   3. ______________________________
   4. ______________________________

2. In addition to meeting the four requirements listed above, contracts concerning real estate are valid only if ___________________________________.

3. Match the following terms:

___ illusory contract	a. intentional deception
___ constructive fraud	b. in writing
___ counteroffer	c. anything of value exchanged
___ duress	d. unintentional misrepresentation
___ actual fraud	e. violence
___ consideration	f. qualified acceptance
___ statute of frauds	g. vague offer

4. Indicate whether each of the following statements is true or false.

   If a person signs a contract without reading it, the contract is unenforceable. T F

   If a contract contains an unlawful provision, it is void. T F

   Consideration can be anything of value, including a promise not to do something. T F

5. A contract that is missing one of the four essential elements is ________.

Exercise 5E

1. It is necessary to take action to rescind a ____________ contract; otherwise, it will be binding.

2. Place each of the following under the appropriate heading shown below:
   a. A contract which one party used fraud to persuade the other party to sign
   b. An agreement that is not supported by consideration
   c. A contract after the statute of limitations has run out
   d. An agreement that has an unlawful objective
   e. A contract signed by a minor

VOID	VOIDABLE	UNENFORCEABLE

3. List three types of situations that will result in an unenforceable contract.
   1. ________________________________
   2. ________________________________
   3. ________________________________

4. In Washington, the statute of limitations period for most written contracts is ____________; for oral contracts the period is ____________.

5. The time limit of the statute of limitations for contract lawsuits begins to run __________________________________ .

Exercise 5F

1. List three ways of discharging a valid contract:
   1. ______________________________
   2. ______________________________
   3. ______________________________

2. When the parties agree to terminate their contract and return any consideration they've exchanged, the termination is called a _______________. If instead they were to terminate the contract without returning the consideration, it would be a _______________.

3. In an assignment, a new party takes the place of one of the original parties to the contract, and that original party is _________________ liable under the contract.

4. True or false? Unless otherwise agreed, one party to a contract can arrange a novation without the other party's consent. T F

5. In the phrase "accord and satisfaction", what do the terms "accord" and "satisfaction" refer to?

   accord: ____

   satisfaction: ____

Exercise 5G

1. The standard remedy for breach of contract is _____________.

2. When damages would be an adequate remedy, a court generally won't order ______________________________.

3. If the buyer breaches the purchase and sale agreement, the earnest money deposit is often treated as ____________________________ .

4. What is the difference between damages and liquidated damages?

____

5. Indicate whether each of the following statements is true or false.

   Any breach of contract entitles the damaged party to a remedy in court. T F

   A party who is damaged by a breach of contract can decide which remedy should be applied. T F

   Specific performance is a common remedy for breach of non-residential real estate purchase and sale contracts. T F

Exercise 5H

1. Match the following terms:

___ specific performance	a.	undoing the contract
___ liquidated damages	b.	an offer to perform as agreed
___ breach	c.	failure to perform, without legal excuse
___ damages	d.	a court order to perform as agreed
___ rescission	e.	monetary compensation
___ tender	f.	agreed on in advance

2. A _______________ is not necessary before filing a lawsuit, if there has been an anticipatory repudiation.

3. Under what circumstances would the failure to perform a contract obligation not constitute a breach of contract?

____

____

Exercise 5I

1. Someone who is interested in buying property may end up signing (circle all that are correct):

   a. an option agreement

   b. a purchase and sale agreement

   c. a listing agreement

   d. a land contract

2. Circle all of the following that are true in regard to an option to purchase real property:

   a. must be in writing

   b. must be recorded

   c. obligates optionor to sell the property to optionee if option is exercised before deadline

   d. obligates optionee to purchase the property if no other bids are received

3. List two reasons why listing agreements should always be put in writing.

   1. ______________________________

   2. ______________________________

4. In a land contract, the buyer is referred to as the ___________, and the seller is called the ___________. The buyer receives the deed to the property when ______________________.

5. List the three important functions served by a purchase and sale agreement.

   1. ______________________________

   2. ______________________________

   3. ______________________________

6. List the parties to each of the following types of contracts.
   a. listing agreement ______________________________
   b. purchase and sale agreement ______________________________
   c. lease ______________________________
   d. escrow instructions ______________________________
   e. option ______________________________

Lesson 5: Workbook Quiz Questions

1. A contract is bilateral if:
   a. each party makes a promise, so that both parties are legally obligated to perform
   b. only one of the parties is legally obligated to perform
   c. it has been put into words (spoken or written)
   d. it is in the process of being performed

2. Once a contract has been fully performed, it is said to be:
   a. executory
   b. executed
   c. unilateral
   d. implied

3. Which of these is one of the four basic elements needed to make a contract valid and legally binding?
   a. A unilateral promise
   b. A counteroffer
   c. Mutual consent
   d. Voidability

4. A contract is voidable if one of the parties:
   a. is a minor
   b. used misrepresentation to persuade the other to enter into it
   c. has the right to rescind it
   d. All of the above

5. In Washington, to have legal capacity to enter into a contract, a person must be:
   a. at least 21 years old
   b. able to read and to sign his or her name
   c. registered with the superior court
   d. mentally competent

6. A contract is not formed if the offer is:
   a. revoked before it is accepted
   b. accepted before it expires
   c. revoked after it is accepted
   d. accepted without any modification of its terms

7. When an offeree makes a counteroffer:
   a. no contract is formed unless the original offeror accepts the counteroffer
   b. the original offeror is required to accept the offeree's modified terms
   c. if the original offeror does not accept the offeree's modifications, they have a binding contract on the terms originally offered
   d. it creates a binding contract on the offeree's modified terms, unless the modifications are unreasonable

8. A contract signed under duress:
   a. can be rescinded by either party
   b. is voidable by the party who was forced to sign
   c. does not fulfill the requirements of the statute of frauds
   d. is treated as an implied contract

9. Consideration is:
   a. not required for contracts that have been put into writing
   b. not required if the contract has a lawful objective
   c. something of value exchanged by the contracting parties
   d. formal execution of the contract in the presence of at least two witnesses

10. The statute of frauds applies to:
    a. a purchase and sale agreement for a house
    b. a purchase and sale agreement for vacant land
    c. a listing agreement for a piece of commercial real estate
    d. All of the above

11. A real estate purchase and sale agreement will not fulfill the requirements of the statute of frauds unless:
    a. it is signed by the parties to be bound
    b. each party swears that all statements made are true and correct
    c. it is a formal document drawn up by a lawyer
    d. it is signed in the presence of at least two witnesses

12. A void contract:
    a. may be disregarded, because it has no legal effect
    b. is enforceable unless rescinded within two weeks after it is signed
    c. is unenforceable unless rescinded within a reasonable time after it is signed
    d. None of the above

13. If no action is taken to rescind a voidable contract:
    a. it automatically becomes void
    b. a court may declare that the contract has been ratified
    c. if cannot be enforced until the statute of frauds expires
    d. it must be assigned to another party

14. A statute of limitations:
    a. limits the amount of consideration a party to a contract can be required to pay
    b. limits the number of contracts a person can enter into in one year
    c. sets a deadline for filing a lawsuit
    d. sets a deadline for fulfilling the terms of a contract

15. A valid, enforceable contract may be discharged by:
    a. the statute of frauds
    b. consideration
    c. breach of contract
    d. agreement between the parties

16. When a contract is rescinded:
    a. performance must be completed within six months
    b. the parties return any consideration that has been exchanged
    c. a new party is substituted for one of the original parties
    d. All of the above

17. The buyer and seller agreed that they would terminate their purchase and sale agreement and the seller would keep the earnest money deposit the buyer had given him. This is an example of:
    a. revocation
    b. novation
    c. rescission
    d. cancellation

18. As a general rule, a contract can be assigned from one party to another:

    a. unless a clause in the contract prohibits assignment
    b. unless the assignee is not a good credit risk
    c. only if there is no other way to avoid breach of contract
    d. only with the written consent of all parties

19. The key difference between an assignment and a novation is that in a novation:

    a. the withdrawing party is released from liability
    b. the withdrawing party remains secondarily liable
    c. the other party's consent is not required
    d. the statute of frauds does not apply

20. In the contract, the parties agree in advance that $10,000 will serve as full compensation to be paid in the event that one of the parties defaults. This sum is called:

    a. cancellation damages
    b. consideration
    c. specific performance
    d. liquidated damages

21. Which of these is a legal action that compels the party who has breached the contract to perform as agreed?

    a. Rescission
    b. Damages
    c. Specific performance
    d. Full performance

22. Specific performance is usually only available as a remedy for breach of contract:

    a. if the parties agree to it in advance
    b. when there has been an anticipatory repudiation
    c. when the breach was malicious and unjustified
    d. when monetary damages would not be sufficient compensation

23. One party's unconditional offer to the other party to perform the contract as agreed is called:

    a. a meeting of the minds
    b. a counteroffer
    c. a tender
    d. an anticipatory repudiation

24. An option to purchase real estate:

    a. must be in writing
    b. does not require consideration
    c. creates a lien against the property
    d. All of the above

25. If the optionee fails to exercise the option within the specified time:

    a. the option is automatically extended for a similar period
    b. the option expires automatically
    c. the optionor can sue for breach of contract
    d. the optionor is entitled to specific performance

Lesson 6

Agency Law

Exercise 6A

1. Match the term in the left column with the correct definition or description on the right:

___ principal	a.	authorized to act by the principal
___ agent	b.	authorizes another person to act for him or her

2. Stanley hires Carmen as his real estate broker to sell his house. Carmen shows the house to Frank, who decides to make an offer on the property. Match each of the parties in this transaction to the appropriate term below:

___ principal	a.	Frank
___ agent	b.	Stanley
___ third party	c.	Carmen

3. Match each type of agent with an appropriate example:

___ universal agent	a.	real estate broker
___ general agent	b.	legal guardian
___ special agent	c.	property manager

4. True or false? A principal is legally bound by the authorized actions of his or her agent, just as if the actions were those of the principal. T F

5. Of the three classifications of agents, which one has the greatest degree of authority?
   a. Special agent
   b. General agent
   c. Universal agent

Exercise 6B

1. True or false? The only requirement for creating an agency relationship is the consent of both parties. T F
2. From the following list, choose the three common law methods for creating an agency relationship:
   a. estoppel
   b. independent contractor
   c. implied action
   d. express principal
   e. express agreement
   f. ratification
3. True or false? Because of the statute of frauds, an unwritten agency agreement has no legal effect. T F
4. Under what circumstances will a seller agency be created?

   ____

5. When a licensee renders brokerage services to a buyer, that licensee will not become the buyer's agent under what circumstances?

   ____

Exercise 6C

1. A principal is bound by the acts of his or her agent that are within the scope of the agent's ____________________, but not by acts outside of it.

2. The scope of an agent's authority includes: (circle all that apply)

   a. express actual authority

   b. implied actual authority

   c. apparent authority

3. An agent has the authority that is required to carry out acts that were expressly authorized. This authority is called ______________________________.

4. Indicate whether each of the following statements is true or false.

   An agent is not liable to third parties for acts that are within the scope of the agent's authority. T F

   A principal is not bound by acts that are within the scope of the agent's authority. T F

   If a third party is harmed by the acts of an agent, the agent will be liable regardless of whether the principal authorized the acts. T F

Exercise 6D

1. Licensees owe all parties certain duties, regardless of their agency relationships. These duties are imposed by Washington's ____________________.

2. Match the duty in the left column to the statement in the right column that describes a violation of that duty:

___ reasonable care and skill	a.	Broker Boyd deposits earnest money received on behalf of his client in Boyd's personal account
___ honesty and good faith	b.	Adams fails to tell the buyer that the roof has a serious leak
___ accounting	c.	Carson neglects to obtain all the necessary signatures on a purchase and sale agreement
___ agency disclosure	d.	Dillon lies to both parties to get a bigger commission
___ disclosure of material facts	e.	Listing Broker Evans discloses to a potential buyer that he will represent the buyer's best interests

3. Which of the following would be considered material information? (More than one answer can be correct.)
   a. The city's plans to build a park next to the property in the next six months
   b. The fact that the previous homeowner died of AIDS
   c. The fact that a serious crime was committed on the property one year ago
   d. The fact that the property is in a flood zone

4. True or false? A licensee can be sued based on his or her opinions or puffing.
   T F

5. What is the purpose of the Washington law that requires disclosure of agency representation?

   ____

6. A licensee has no duty to verify information passed on by the ______________ or obtained from a ______________________________.

Exercise 6E

1. What are a real estate agent's duties to his or her principal under the provisions of Washington's real estate agency law?

   1. ______________________________
   2. ______________________________
   3. ______________________________
   4. ______________________________
   5. ______________________________

2. If a real estate agent breaches a fiduciary duty to a principal, what are the potential consequences for the agent?

   1. ______________________________
   2. ______________________________
   3. ______________________________
   4. ______________________________

3. Broker Sharon has a listing for Brian's property. Sharon's sister Susan wants to make an offer on the property. What should Sharon do?

   ____

4. Indicate whether each of the following statements is true or false.

   An agent does not need to disclose an inadvertent dual agency. T F

   Dual agency is usually a good idea, since both parties can be represented for the cost of a single commission. T F

   The duty of accounting requires brokers to make all of their business records available for inspection by sellers who have listed with the broker. T F

5. If a seller sues a broker for breach of an agency duty, which of the following remedies is least likely to be applied by the court?

   a. Damages
   b. Specific performance
   c. Rescission

Exercise 6F

1. Match the items from Column A to the correct answers in Column B:

___	an agent's puffing	a.	what a licensee owes to each party
___	duty of honesty and good faith	b.	licensee is required to disclose this to any party
___	tort	c.	the type of lawsuit a buyer can bring against a broker for misrepresentation
___	material fact	d.	a party usually cannot sue on the basis of this

2. A tort is a breach of a duty that does not arise from a contract, but is imposed by ___________.

3. A seller (principal) can sometimes be sued for his agent's torts, but can the agent be sued for torts committed by his principal?

   Yes No

4. When can a principal be held liable for the torts of his or her agent?

   1. ____

   2. ____

5. Describe the warranty of authority rule.

   ____

   ____

Exercise 6G

1. Which of the following are required for a broker to be entitled to compensation? (More than one may be correct.)
   a. Accounting
   b. Proper licensing
   c. Tort liability
   d. Written employment contract
   e. Fulfillment of the employment contract terms

2. True or false? In most cases, a broker is entitled to reimbursement from the seller for expenses related to marketing the seller's property. T F

3. If the seller tells her broker that her property is not in a flood hazard zone, and the broker passes this information on to the buyer without verifying it, who will be liable if it turns out that the property is in fact within a flood hazard zone?

   ____

Exercise 6H

1. Under common law, an agency agreement can be terminated by the acts of the parties in one of four ways:
   1. by mutual ____________
   2. revocation by the ____________
   3. renunciation by the ____________
   4. ____________ of the agency term

2. Revocation or renunciation before the specified termination date may constitute breach of ____________.

3. True or false? The agent's authority ends automatically on the termination date set by the agreement. T F

4. Dan and Flora agree that Flora will try to find a buyer for Dan's house before Christmas. Under common law rules, each of the occurrences listed below will terminate the agency agreement between Flora and Dan. Place the occurrences under the appropriate headings:

   a. Flora finds a buyer, and the sale closes.

   b. The property has not sold by Christmas.

   c. Dan files for bankruptcy.

   d. The house is destroyed by fire.

   e. Flora and Dan agree to terminate their agreement because the market is slow.

   f. Dan tells Flora he no longer wants her to try to sell his house.

   g. Flora tells Dan she is taking a new job and will no longer be able to try to sell his house.

Termination by Acts of the Parties	Termination by Operation of Law

5. Under Washington's real estate agency law, an agency relationship terminates:

   1. ______________________________

   2. ______________________________

   3. ______________________________

Lesson 6: Workbook Quiz Questions

1. In a typical real estate transaction, there is an agency relationship between:
   a. the seller (principal) and the listing broker (agent)
   b. the seller (principal) and the buyer (agent)
   c. the seller (agent) and the buyer (principal)
   d. the buyer (principal) and the listing broker (agent)

2. A special agent is authorized to:
   a. do anything that can be lawfully delegated to a representative
   b. conduct a specific transaction
   c. handle all of the principal's affairs in one or more areas
   d. enter into contracts on the principal's behalf

3. In order for a valid agency relationship to exist, there must be:
   a. an enforceable contract
   b. consideration
   c. the consent of both the principal and the agent
   d. All of the above

4. A real estate salesperson is:
   a. the principal of a subagent
   b. a subagent of a third party
   c. the agent of a buyer
   d. the agent of his or her broker

5. With respect to dealings with third parties, an agent is usually considered to warrant:
   a. the principal's capacity to perform
   b. all the information the principal provides concerning the property
   c. the validity of the seller's title to the property
   d. his or her authority to act on the principal's behalf

6. In general, an agency relationship can be established by express agreement:
   a. even if the agreement is not put into writing
   b. only if the agreement is in writing and recorded
   c. only if the agreement is supported by consideration
   d. only if the agreement is ratified by the principal

7. If a principal gives approval after the fact to unauthorized actions, an agency relationship is established by:
   a. ratification
   b. estoppel
   c. negotiation
   d. implied actual authority

8. In a real estate transaction, a buyer agency relationship may be created:
   a. by written agreement only
   b. by providing real estate brokerage services to the buyer
   c. only if the real estate agent is compensated by the buyer
   d. only if the principal requires the agent to work according to a set schedule

9. Once an agency relationship has been established, the principal is liable for the acts of the agent:
   a. in all cases
   b. only if the agent is estopped from denying agency authority
   c. when the agent's acts are authorized by the principal
   d. that are within the scope of the agent's ratification

10. A licensee owes to all parties, regardless of whom the licensee represents, the duty of:
    a. loyalty
    b. confidentiality
    c. immediately disclosing all conflicts of interest
    d. reasonable care and skill

11. The law requires an agent to serve the best interests of the principal, because the agent is:
    a. a fiduciary
    b. an independent contractor
    c. an employee
    d. a trustee

12. It would be a breach of duty for an agent to:
    a. make a secret profit from the agency
    b. accept trust funds on behalf of the principal
    c. buy property from the principal
    d. refuse to reveal confidential information to a third party

13. Under Washington's real estate agency law, if a third party provides information to the agent:
    a. the agent must not disclose the information to the principal
    b. the principal is deemed to know the information only if the agent actually discloses it to the principal
    c. it is not necessary for the agent to disclose the information to the principal
    d. the agent should withdraw from the transaction

14. It is not improper for a real estate agent to buy the principal's property as long as the agent:
    a. knows the principal is in a hurry to sell
    b. is paying a fair price for the property
    c. has disclosed the true value of the property
    d. None of the above

15. Dual agency is:
    a. improper unless the buyer pays the agent's commission
    b. improper unless the buyer is a friend or relative of the agent
    c. not improper if both agents are paid the same amount
    d. not improper if both principals give their informed, written consent

16. A buyer is not likely to win a lawsuit against a seller's real estate agent:
    a. for failure to disclose known latent defects
    b. if the suit is based on opinions, predictions, or puffing
    c. unless the seller is also suing the agent
    d. unless the suit involves implied dual agency

17. A latent defect is a problem with the property that:
    a. the seller is not aware of
    b. the buyer has chosen to accept "as is"
    c. is deliberately concealed from the buyer
    d. would not be discovered in an ordinary inspection

18. A licensee has a duty to investigate:
    a. only those things the licensee has specifically agreed to investigate
    b. and verify all information passed on by the seller
    c. only those latent defects the seller is aware of
    d. None of the above

19. After an agency relationship between a real estate broker and a seller is terminated:
    a. the broker is no longer authorized to represent the seller
    b. the broker can make use of confidential information obtained through the agency
    c. the broker is still required to present all offers to the seller
    d. All of the above

20. An agency relationship may terminate:
    a. only if there is no termination date in the agency agreement
    b. only if the agent has proven to be incompetent or untrustworthy
    c. only with the agent's written consent
    d. with the mutual consent of the parties

21. Seller knows her property was the site of a suicide three years ago. She relayed this information to her listing agent. Under Washington's real estate agency law, the listing agent:
    a. must disclose this information to the buyer
    b. must refuse to represent the seller unless the seller agrees to disclose this information to the buyer
    c. does not have to disclose this fact to the buyer because it is not a material fact
    d. must indepedently verify this information and then pass it on to the buyer

22. If an agency agreement does not state a termination date:
    a. it is deemed to expire within a reasonable time
    b. the agent can terminate the agency without liability for damages
    c. the principal can terminate the agency without liability for damages
    d. All of the above

23. A principal entered into an agency agreement that was to last for a period of three months. Two weeks later, the principal died of natural causes. Which of the following is true?
    a. The principal's heirs are required to honor the terms of the agency agreement
    b. The agency continues unless the principal's heirs choose to revoke it
    c. The agency relationship terminated automatically when the principal died
    d. The agency terminated as soon as the agent was informed of the principal's death

24. An agency relationship terminates automatically:
    a. when its purpose has been fulfilled
    b. if either the principal or the agent is charged with a felony
    c. if a lawsuit is filed against either the principal or the agent
    d. at the end of one year

25. The owners of an apartment building hire a real estate broker as the property manager. If the owners later sell the building, their agency relationship with the property manager:
    a. is automatically transferred to the new owner
    b. terminates due to extinction of the subject matter
    c. can be terminated by the former owners without liability to the property manager
    d. continues unless terminated by the property manager

Lesson 7

Agency Relationships

Exercise 7A

1. What is meant by the expression "inadvertent dual agency"?

    ____

2. In a typical real estate transaction, there may be as many as four different licensees involved. List the four types of licensees.

    1. ______________
    2. ______________
    3. ______________
    4. ______________

3. Define the following terms.

    Agent ______________

    Listing Broker ______________

    Selling Broker ______________

    Cooperating Broker ______________

4. Match the following definitions to the real estate term:

___ in-house sale	a. when the buyer and seller are brought together by agents working for different brokers
___ client	b. when the buyer and seller are brought together by agents working for the same broker
___ selling salesperson	c. one who engaged the services of an agent
___ customer	d. salesperson who procured the buyer
___ cooperative sale	e. third party

Exercise 7B

1. What difference does it make whether or not an agency relationship exists between a licensee and a party to a transaction?

   ____

2. Buyers, sellers, and agents must all be aware of the nature of any agency relationships in a transaction. Why is this so important to:

   buyers and sellers? ____

   agents? ____

3. Much of the confusion surrounding agency relationships was the result of a listing agreement clause known as the ____ ________________. Even though this clause was later replaced by an offer of ________________________________, the confusion still remained.

4. Under the old unilateral offer of subagency, selling agents were considered to be:

   a. the buyer's agent
   b. subagents of the seller
   c. subagents of the listing salesperson
   d. the buyer's agent only in in-house transactions

5. Under the terms of Washington's real estate agency legislation, licensees who work with a buyer automatically represent the _____________ unless there is a _________________________ to the contrary.

Exercise 7C

1. List the four basic types of relationships that may exist between a real estate agent and a buyer or seller.
   1. ____
   2. ____
   3. ____
   4. ____

2. The most common method for creating a seller agency in a real estate transaction is ____________________________.

3. List two services that a listing agent can provide to prospective buyers without violating the agent's duties to the seller.
   1. ____
   2. ____

4. Why is a listing agent permitted to provide these services to prospective buyers?

   ____

5. If a buyer discloses confidential information to the seller's listing agent (circle all that apply):
   a. the agent has a duty to disclose the information to the seller
   b. the agent should not disclose the information to the seller without permission from the agent's broker
   c. the agent should immediately explain the agency relationship between the agent and the seller

Exercise 7D

1. Most buyer agency relationships are created automatically when the agent first ______________________________. However, a buyer and an agent may also enter into an agency contract called ___________________________________ ________________.

2. List six terms that are commonly included in contracts between buyers and their agents.
   1. ____
   2. ____
   3. ____
   4. ____
   5. ____
   6. ____

3. What is the single most significant benefit of buyer agency to the buyer?

   ____

4. Why does a buyer who enters into an agency agreement with an agent have access to more properties?

   ____

Exercise 7E

1. Why would a seller be willing to agree to pay a commission to a buyer's agent?

   ____

2. Indicate whether each of the following statements is true or false.

   A retainer paid to a buyer's agent is usually non-refundable. T F

   If a buyer's agent ends up earning a commission under a representation agreement, any retainer paid by the buyer is usually credited against the commission. T F

   Most buyer agency agreements specify that the agent will be paid an hourly fee. T F

3. Why might a buyer's agent prefer to be paid directly by the buyer, rather than receive a split of the commission paid by the seller?

   ____

4. The most common method of compensating a buyer's agent is with a ______________________. This method is provided for in most ______________________.

5. List three methods of payment that are commonly used in buyer agency agreements.

   1. ____________________
   2. ____________________
   3. ____________________

Exercise 7F

1. Why is the use of dual agency discouraged?

   ____

2. What is the most common means of creating a dual agency?

   ____

3. Indicate whether each of the following statements is true or false.

   The only proper way to handle a dual agency is to have both the listing and the selling salesperson act as dual agents and the broker act as a seller's agent. T F

   Before agreeing to act as a dual agent, an agent must have the informed written consent of both parties. T F

   Dual agency is a violation of the license law unless the buyer is a close relative or associate of the agent. T F

4. An agent is in violation of the real estate license law if he or she acts as a dual agent without ____________________.

5. The situation where an agent claims to act only as a facilitator and refuses to take on any agency responsibilities is known as ____________. A licensee acting in this capacity may not waive his or her ______________ to the parties to the transaction.

Exercise 7G

1. Indicate whether each of the following statements is true or false.

   The listing agent must make an agency disclosure to both the seller and the buyer. T F

   The selling agent must make an agency disclosure to both the seller and the buyer. T F

   Agency disclosures must be in writing, in the purchase and sale agreement or in a separate document. T F

2. Fill in the steps a dual agent must follow to ensure proper dual agency disclosure:

   1. ____________________
   2. ____________________
   3. ____________________
   4. ____________________

3. Green is buying Brown's house. Both are represented by agents working for Broker White. White discloses to both parties that she will be working as a dual agent and gives them both a copy of the agency law pamphlet. Green and Brown give White their written consent to the dual agency.
   a. The dual agency is lawful because a broker involved in an in-house transaction has the consent of the parties by law, no matter what disclosures are made or what consents are given
   b. The dual agency is unlawful because a broker can never act as a dual agent unless her salespeople are also acting as dual agents
   c. The dual agency is lawful because White disclosed everything she was required to disclose
   d. The dual agency is unlawful because White did not disclose the terms of her compensation

---

Exercise 7H

1. The most important antitrust law was passed in 1890 and is known as ________ ______________________________.

2. What are the three main categories of activities that are prohibited by antitrust laws?
   1. ____
   2. ____
   3. ____

3. Which of the following could be considered in violation of antitrust laws? (Circle all that apply.)
   a. At a meeting of her salespeople, a broker announces that she is raising her commission rates
   b. A professional real estate association publishes a list of the average commission rates charged by its members
   c. A listing broker tells the selling broker what the amount of the commission is
   d. A broker has the commission rate preprinted on her listing agreement forms

4. In the context of the real estate business, a group boycott is defined as ________
____.

5. True or false? All list-back agreements are automatically violations of the antitrust laws. T F

Lesson 7: Workbook Quiz Questions

1. If a buyer does not understand that a listing agent is representing the seller in a transaction:

   a. the agent can take advantage of this fact to get a better price for the seller, and therefore a higher commission
   b. there is a potential for a lawsuit by the buyer against the agent
   c. the agent is obligated to act as a dual agent
   d. the agent has no responsibility to clarify the situation to the buyer

2. In order to alleviate confusion among buyers and sellers regarding agency representation issues, many states, including Washington, enacted laws that:

   a. require agents to disclose to the parties whom they are representing in the transaction
   b. prohibit agents from representing buyers in residential transactions
   c. require brokers to be licensed as either seller's agents or buyer's agents
   d. require agents to act as seller's agents if they are members of a multiple listing service

3. In the absence of a written agreement, the party who is represented by a licensee is:

   a. up to the agent's broker
   b. determined by the real estate commissioner
   c. determined by Washington's real estate agency law
   d. automatically the seller

4. The definition of the term "agent" is:

   a. a person who has a valid real estate license
   b. someone who is authorized to represent another in dealings with third parties
   c. anyone who acts as a real estate broker
   d. someone who works for a real estate broker

5. In a real estate transaction, the agent's client is:

   a. the agent's principal
   b. the agent's customer
   c. the seller
   d. the buyer

6. The selling salesperson in a real estate transaction:

   a. is the salesperson who takes the listing
   b. always represents the seller
   c. may not accept compensation from the seller unless he or she is acting as the seller's agent
   d. is the salesperson who procures a buyer for the sale

7. Under the terms of Washington's real estate agency law, a licensee who provides services to a buyer is likely to represent:

   a. the buyer
   b. the seller
   c. both the buyer and the seller
   d. no one in the transaction

8. The most common method for creating a seller agency relationship is:
   a. payment of a commission
   b. a written listing agreement
   c. submitting a listing to a multiple listing service
   d. words or conduct of the parties indicating an intent to create an agency

9. Which of the following statements about seller's agents is not true?
   a. A seller's agent must use his or her best efforts to promote the interests of the seller
   b. A seller's agent may not provide any services to a buyer without entering into a dual agency agreement
   c. A seller's agent may assist the buyer in obtaining financing and preparing the offer to purchase
   d. A seller's agent owes the buyer the duty of disclosure of material facts

10. A real estate salesperson is ordinarily considered to be:
    a. an agent of his or her broker's clients
    b. a principal in the transaction
    c. a dual agent, unless the transaction is an in-house transaction
    d. an agent of his or her broker

11. In an in-house sale:
    a. the listing is not submitted to the MLS
    b. the compensation must be paid from the principal directly to the broker's salespeople
    c. the buyer and seller are brought together by salespeople working for the same broker
    d. All of the above

12. Harrison, who works for Broker Yates, obtains a listing for a property and submits it to the multiple listing service. Bailey works for Broker Opstad, who is a member of the MLS. If Bailey finds a buyer for the property listed by Harrison, who would be considered the cooperating broker?
    a. Harrison
    b. Yates
    c. Bailey
    d. Opstad

13. Harrison, who works for Broker Yates, obtains a listing for a property and submits it to the multiple listing service. Baker, who also works for Yates, finds a buyer for the property. In this situation:
    a. Baker would be considered the seller's agent
    b. Broker Yates is a dual agent, because it is an in-house sale
    c. Baker must be careful not to give the buyer advice, such as suggesting how much to offer for the property
    d. Baker would be considered a dual agent

14. Until recently, it was common for listing agreements to contain a "unilateral offer of subagency" if they were going to be submitted to a multiple listing service. Under the terms of such a listing agreement, a member of the MLS who procured a buyer for the listed property:
    a. was automatically considered to be a subagent of the listing broker
    b. was automatically considered to be a subagent of the selling broker
    c. was automatically considered to be a subagent of the seller
    d. was automatically considered to be a subagent of the buyer

15. If a listing agreement states that members of the multiple listing service will act as cooperating agents, it means that members of the MLS:
    a. must cooperate with the listing broker
    b. are free to choose which party (if any) they represent
    c. have an agency relationship with the seller
    d. may act as buyer's agents if they are willing to accept a lower commission split

16. From a buyer's point of view, which of the following is not an advantage of a buyer agency relationship with a real estate agent?
    a. Access to a wider range of properties
    b. Assistance in negotiating the terms of sale
    c. Expert advice in regard to confidential matters
    d. Cost savings, since buyer's agents don't work on a commission basis

17. From a broker's point of view, which of the following is an advantage of the legal presumption of buyer agency?
    a. Assurance of earning a commission
    b. Increased likelihood of conflicts of interest
    c. Less confusion about which party the agent is representing
    d. Avoidance of liability for misrepresentations

18. A buyer's agent is most commonly compensated by:
    a. the buyer, through payment of a commission
    b. the seller, through a commission split
    c. the buyer, through payment of a flat fee
    d. the seller, through payment of a flat fee

19. If a licensee chooses to act as a non-agent in a transaction, the licensee:
    a. still owes general duties of disclosure, reasonable care, and accounting to both parties
    b. owes no duties to either party
    c. can withhold material facts from either party
    d. does not really need a real estate license at all

20. An agent who is representing a buyer runs the risk of a conflict of interest if she:
    a. shows the buyer a property that is listed by her
    b. shows the buyer a property that is not offered through a multiple listing service
    c. shows the buyer a property that is For Sale By Owner
    d. shows the buyer a property that is listed by another broker

21. In a dual agency:
    a. the agent represents both the buyer and the seller in the same transaction
    b. there is an inherent conflict of interest between the agent's responsibilities to the buyer and the agent's responsibilities to the seller
    c. the buyer and seller must be informed about the duties owed by the dual agent to the principals
    d. All of the above

22. Which of the following statements about dual agency is not true?
    a. Dual agency is created automatically in an in-house transaction
    b. Dual agency is illegal in Washington
    c. Dual agency is widely discouraged because of the inherent potential for conflict of interest
    d. Dual agency requires comprehensive disclosure to both parties the agent is representing

23. All of the following activities could be considered unlawful price fixing in violation of antitrust laws, except:
    a. a discussion between two competing brokers about their respective commission rates
    b. publication of a report on commission rates charged by members of a multiple listing service
    c. a discussion between a broker and a salesperson working for the broker regarding commission rates charged by the brokerage
    d. an announcement by a broker that he intends to raise his commission rates in the coming year

24. Antitrust laws prohibit activities that tend to limit competition in the marketplace, including:
    a. price fixing
    b. group boycotts
    c. tie-in arrangements
    d. All of the above

25. Washington law requires a selling agent to disclose whom she is representing:
    a. to the buyer, but not to the seller
    b. to the seller, but not to the buyer
    c. to both parties, no later than 3 days before the closing date of the sale
    d. to the buyer before preparing an offer to purchase, and to the seller before presenting the offer for acceptance

Lesson 8

Transfer of Real Property

Exercise 8A

1. Voluntary alienation can be by the following methods:

   a. ______________________________

   b. ______________________________

   c. ______________________________

   d. ______________________________

2. Title to all privately owned land in the United States can be traced back to a ________________________ from the federal government.

3. In order to transfer real property to another person, a private landowner uses:

   a. a patent

   b. a covenant

   c. a deed

   d. a grantor

4. The covenant of quiet enjoyment is:

   a. a promise that no lawful claim will disturb the grantee's possession

   b. a noise ordinance

   c. the only warranty of a quitclaim deed

   d. a restrictive covenant that can be legally included in a deed by the developer of a subdivision

Exercise 8B

1. Three types of deeds commonly used in Washington are the:

   a. ______________________________

   b. ______________________________

   c. ______________________________

2. Match the description with the deed:

___ warranty deed	a. conveys title "as is" and gives the grantee no recourse against the grantor
___ quitclaim deed	b. contains five covenants warranting against defects in title
___ special warranty deed	c. offers no warranties as to defects that arose before grantor's ownership

3. True or false? If there is a defect in title at the time of transfer under a warranty deed, but that defect is later cured, the deed is void. T F

Exercise 8C

1. Which of the following is not a requirement for a valid deed?

   a. The grantor's signature

   b. Description of the property to be conveyed

   c. The signature of the grantee

   d. The deed must be in writing

2. True or false? When a married couple sells community property, both of them need to sign the deed. T F

3. The document in which a person appoints someone to be his or her attorney in fact is known as a ______________________________.

4. The state law that requires a conveyance of real property to be in writing is the ______________________________________.

5. Once there is a valid deed, three additional steps are necessary to convey real property. They are:
   1. ____________________________
   2. ____________________________
   3. ____________________________

6. Proper delivery of a deed is presumed if the _________ has been recorded, or if it is in the possession of the ___________________.

Exercise 8D

1. The habendum clause is also known as the:
   a. granting clause
   b. "to have and to hold" clause
   c. acknowledgment

2. Although useful, a recital of ________________________ is not required for a valid deed.

3. Wills, deeds, and patents are all methods of voluntary _____________________.

4. True or false? In Washington, although a will spoken on the testator's deathbed can be valid, it cannot transfer real estate. T F

5. *Rachel* made a will leaving her *house* to her daughter and her *cars* to her son. She named her *sister* to carry out the terms of the will. Match each of the following terms to one of the italicized words in the sentence above.

   Executor _______________

   Devise _________________

   Testator ________________

   Bequest ________________

Exercise 8E

1. A county ordinance requires a subdivision developer to transfer some of the land in the subdivision for public streets. This is called:
    a. voluntary alienation
    b. intestate succession
    c. condemnation
    d. statutory dedication

2. An heir acquires property through ________________ succession.

3. Government power to buy property from a private owner is the power of:
    a. statutory dedication
    b. voluntary alienation
    c. eminent domain
    d. just compensation

4. The basic rules concerning condemnation of property by the government are found in the ________________________.

5. Choose the TWO requirements for exercising the power of eminent domain.
    a. Just compensation
    b. Legal partition
    c. Foreclosure
    d. Public use
    e. Escheat

6. True or false? Just compensation is usually fair market value. T F

7. True or false? A private property owner can institute an inverse condemnation lawsuit. T F

Exercise 8F

1. Three types of lawsuits that can transfer title to property are:
   1. ____________________________
   2. ____________________________
   3. ____________________________
2. A legal procedure to remove a cloud on the title is called:
   a. quitclaim action
   b. quiet title action
   c. adverse possession
   d. voluntary dedication
3. A court can order physical division of property in a ______________________ action.

Exercise 8G

1. To meet the five requirements for adverse possession in Washington, possession must be:
   1. ______________________________
   2. ______________________________
   3. ______________________________
   4. ______________________________
   5. ______________________________
2. True or false? Someone who mistakenly believes he or she has title to the property can acquire title by adverse possession. T F
3. An example of possession under color of title is possession under a defective ________________.

4. The usual period required for adverse possession in Washington is ____________ years.

5. Adding together successive periods of occupation by a series of adverse possessors to meet the statutory requirement is known as ________________.

6. True or false? In order for an adverse possessor who has met all the requirements of adverse possession to gain title, he or she must bring an action in court.
T F

Exercise 8H

1. Match the terms with the correct definitions below:

___ alluvion	a. any addition to real property from natural or artificial causes
___ avulsion	b. waterborne soil deposits
___ accession	c. a violent tearing away of land by flowing water
___ reliction	d. exposure of land as water recedes gradually

2. The addition of fixtures to real property is one type of ______________________.

3. Adams owns the land on the south side of Rushing River, and Burr owns the land on the north shore. As a result of a flood, the river suddenly changes course to the south, so that it now runs through the center of Adams' property. Indicate whether each of the following statements is true or false.

   This is an example of accretion. T F

   Burr now has title to the part of Adams' property that now lies north of the river.
   T F

   Adams must take action to reclaim his lost property, or he will lose title to it.
   T F

Exercise 8I

1. Before a deed is recorded, the signatures must be ____________________.

2. Recording is accomplished by filing a deed or other document with the county recorder in the county where:

    a. the purchase and sale agreement was signed

    b. the previous sale of the property was recorded

    c. the property is located

3. The county recorder's office maintains two indexes: a ______________ index and a _______________ index.

4. These indexes are used to conduct title _______________. They can also be used to trace a _______________ of title.

5. True or false? The most important effect of recording is to give actual notice of the recorded transaction. T F

6. Which of the following documents has no legal effect if it is not recorded?

    a. Commercial lease

    b. Lis pendens

    c. Warranty deed

    d. Special warranty deed

7. Joseph deeds the same piece of property to two people: to Frank in May 1992 and then to Lila in October 1992. Lila recorded her deed in October, and Frank recorded his in November. Between Lila and Frank, who has title?

    ____

Exercise 8J

1. A title insurance policy protects the policyholder against:
   a. property damage
   b. losses due to title defects
   c. adverse possession
   d. avulsion

2. Before issuing a policy, the title insurance company will conduct a __________ __________ and will prepare a preliminary ____________________.

3. The two main types of title insurance policies are:
   1. ______________________________
   2. ______________________________

4. A title insurance policy lasts:
   a. one year
   b. for the life of the grantor
   c. until a title defect is discovered
   d. until the policyholder's interest in the property is extinguished

5. True or false? Premiums on title insurance are paid monthly, with the mortgage payments. T F

6. Standard coverage title insurance protects against which of the following risks? (Circle all that are correct.)
   a. Encumbrances of record
   b. Encroachments
   c. Fraud
   d. Government action

7. Which type of policy insures against interests that would be disclosed by physical inspection of the property? ____________________

8. Which type of coverage is the mortgagee's policy that lenders generally require?
   a. Extended coverage
   b. Standard coverage

Exercise 8K

1. List three types of legal descriptions:
   1. ______________________________
   2. ______________________________
   3. ______________________________
2. Boundaries in a metes and bounds description are described by reference to what three things?
   1. ______________________________
   2. ______________________________
   3. ______________________________
3. Place each item under the appropriate headings.
   a. due west
   b. 430 feet
   c. to the center of Smith Creek
   d. oak tree
   e. Smith Creek
   f. S 15º E

Monuments	Courses	Distances

Exercise 8L

1. Shade in the NW $^1/_4$ of the SW $^1/_4$ of the SE $^1/_4$.

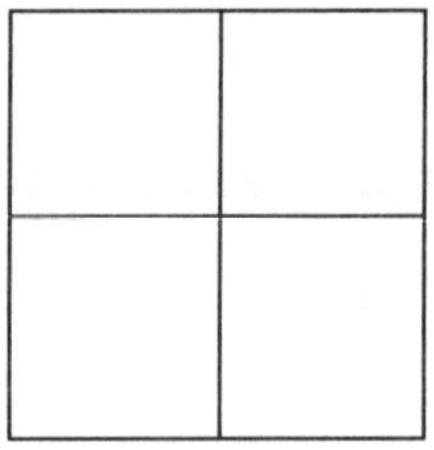

2. Shade in the SE $^1/_4$ of the SE $^1/_4$ of the SE $^1/_4$ of the SW $^1/_4$.

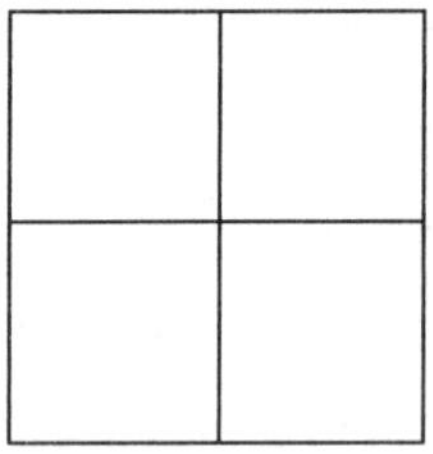

3. The shaded areas are called
______________________.

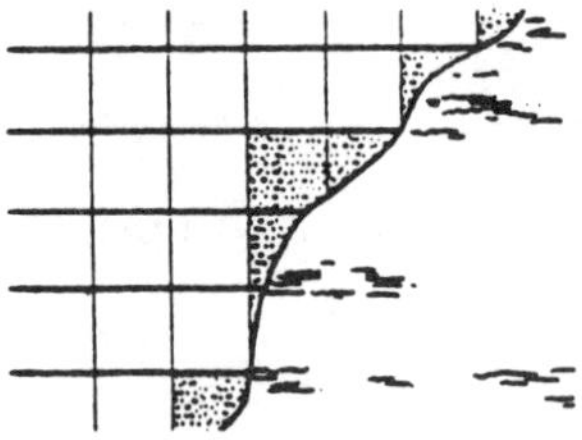

4. The principal meridian used for rectangular survey descriptions in Washington is called the ______________________________________.

Exercise 8M

1. This is an example of a
_________________________.

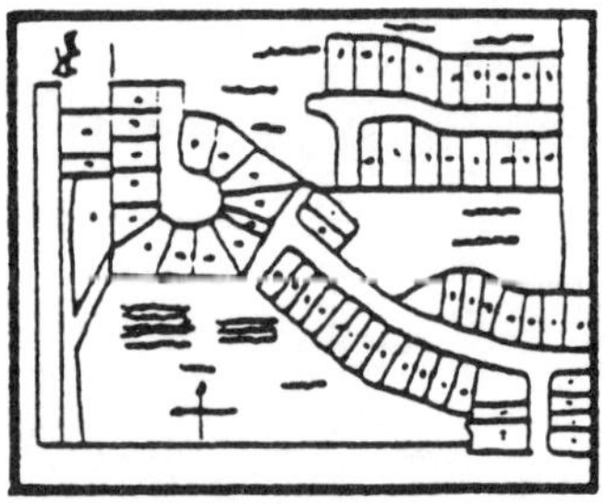

2. In the lot and block method of description, land is described by reference to a ______________________________.

3. Match the terms to the correct description:

___	plat map	a.	numbered from 1 to 36
___	principal meridian	b.	36 square miles
___	used in rural areas	c.	the main north/south line in a grid
___	sections	d.	marks a fixed point
___	monument	e.	shows lots and blocks in a subdivision
___	township	f.	rectangular survey description

3. The system of land description that is most commonly used for urban and suburban properties in Washington is ______________________________.

Lesson 8: Workbook Quiz Questions

1. Transferring ownership from one party to another, by any means, is called:
   a. alienation
   b. conveyance
   c. accession
   d. encumbrance

2. Title to land is passed from the government to a private party with a document called:
   a. a warranty deed
   b. a patent
   c. a covenant of seisin
   d. an acknowledgment

3. The covenants in a general warranty deed warrant against:
   a. any title defects that may arise in the future
   b. title defects that arose only during the grantor's period of ownership
   c. title defects that arose either before or during the grantor's period of ownership
   d. after-acquired title

4. The usual reason for using a quitclaim deed is to:
   a. convey after-acquired title
   b. give the greatest protection to the grantee
   c. warrant that there are no encumbrances
   d. cure clouds on the title

5. In addition to requiring a deed to be in writing, the statute of frauds also requires that the deed must be:
   a. delivered after the grantor's death
   b. recorded before it is acknowledged
   c. signed by the grantee
   d. signed by the grantor

6. A valid deed must contain:
   a. an adequate description of the property
   b. a habendum clause
   c. a recital of consideration
   d. warranties

7. A valid deed transfers title when:
   a. the grantor delivers it to the grantee
   b. it is acknowledged by the grantor
   c. the grantee signs it
   d. it is recorded

8. When a grantor swears before a notary public that his or her signature on the deed is genuine and voluntary, it is called:
   a. delivery
   b. acknowledgment
   c. the covenant of right to convey
   d. execution

9. A testator devises:
   a. a bequest
   b. a codicil
   c. real property
   d. personal property

10. To be valid, a will generally must be:
    a. dated within one year before the testator's death
    b. acknowledged and recorded
    c. drafted by an attorney at law
    d. witnessed by at least two competent witnesses

11. When a person dies without leaving a valid will, his or her property is transferred to heirs through:
    a. intestate succession
    b. escheat
    c. eminent domain
    d. statutory dedication

12. The government's power to condemn private property is called the power of:
    a. eminent domain
    b. dedication
    c. escheat
    d. accession

13. An adverse possessor's use and possession of the land must be:
    a. registered with the county clerk
    b. open and notorious
    c. by permission of the true owner
    d. by permission of the state government

14. To acquire marketable title, an adverse possessor may have to:
    a. record a declaration of escheat
    b. apply for inverse condemnation
    c. file a quiet title action
    d. comply with the rules for statutory dedication

15. When riparian or littoral land is enlarged by the gradual retreat of the body of water, it is called:
    a. seisin
    b. avulsion
    c. accretion
    d. reliction

16. Before a deed can be recorded, it must be:
    a. delivered to the grantee
    b. acknowledged by the grantor
    c. certified by a title company
    d. published in a title report

17. A deed is recorded in order to:
    a. protect against adverse possession
    b. transfer title to the grantee
    c. validate the chain of title for the grantor
    d. provide constructive notice of the grantee's interest

18. A grantee who fails to record his or her deed:
    a. could lose title to a subsequent good faith purchaser
    b. does not take title to the property
    c. allows title to revert to the grantor
    d. will still be listed in the grantor/grantee indexes

19. An extended coverage title insurance policy covers all of the problems a standard coverage policy does, plus:
    a. problems that should be revealed by a property inspection
    b. recorded encumbrances
    c. forged deeds and incompetent grantors
    d. condemnation

20. Title insurance policies never protect a property owner from losses due to:
    a. latent title defects
    b. adverse possession
    c. encroachments
    d. governmental action

21. In a title insurance policy, the title company:
    a. certifies that there are no defects in the grantor's title
    b. agrees to reimburse the policy holder for the defects of record that are excluded from coverage
    c. agrees to indemnify the policy holder against losses due to defects covered by the policy
    d. insures the title only against defects arising during the grantor's period of ownership

22. The method of legal description that involves courses, distances, and a point of beginning is the:

    a. government survey method
    b. rectangular survey method
    c. lot and block method
    d. metes and bounds method

23. In the rectangular survey system, each township:

    a. is assigned a government lot number
    b. is 640 acres
    c. contains 36 sections
    d. measures one square mile

24. When land is subdivided, a plat is:

    a. recorded in the county where the property is located
    b. used instead of title insurance
    c. submitted to the government survey system
    d. no longer necessary

25. When a single-family home in a city subdivision is sold, the property will probably be described in the deed using the:

    a. metes and bounds method
    b. lot and block method
    c. government lot method
    d. township method

Lesson 9

Listing Agreements

Exercise 9A

1. The written contract that sets forth the rights and duties of the seller and the broker is the ____________________ agreement.

2. True or false? A salesperson may fill out and sign a listing agreement. T F

3. In the agency relationship created by the listing agreement, the broker is the ____________ and the seller is the ________________.

4. Which three of the following are required for the listing broker to be entitled to a commission?
   a. The property sold at the original asking price
   b. The seller accepted an offer that met all conditions of the listing agreement
   c. The listing agreement was in writing
   d. The broker fulfilled the terms of the listing agreement
   e. The broker was licensed when he or she provided the brokerage services

5. A buyer who offers to purchase the property on all the terms set forth in the listing agreement is said to be ___________, __________ and ____________.

6. If a seller accepts an offer lower than the asking price, the broker (is / is not) entitled to a commission.

7. True or false? The determination of whether or not a broker is entitled to a commission may depend upon a buyer's financial status. T F

8. If a sale fails to go through because the seller does not have good title to the property, the seller (owes / does not owe) the broker a commission.

Exercise 9B

1. Match the descriptions that apply to each type of listing:

____ open listing	a. to earn a commission, broker must be the procuring cause
____ exclusive agency listing	b. also called a non-exclusive listing
____ exclusive right to sell listing	c. affords broker greatest protection
	d. the type of agreement most commonly used
	e. unilateral contract
	f. broker entitled to commission if anyone other than seller finds buyer

2. Under which type of listing agreement is it most likely that two brokers working on the same sale could end up in a dispute over which one earned the commission?

   ____

3. True or false? With an exclusive right to sell listing, the broker earns a commission no matter who sells the property. T F

4. If a broker puts no effort at all into selling property under an open listing, it (is / is not) a breach of contract.

5. Which types of listing agreements require due diligence from the broker? (Circle all that are correct.)

   a. Exclusive agency

   b. Exclusive right to sell

   c. Open

6. Even if a broker's promise to market the property is not stated explicitly in an exclusive listing, the promise will be ________________.

Exercise 9C

1. Every listing agreement must:

   ________________ the property

   include a promise to ______________________ the broker

   be ___________________ and signed by the ______________________

2. Although only a clear identification of the property is required, it is a good idea to include a complete ____________________________________ of the property in the listing agreement.

3. Net listings state the _______ amount a seller will accept from the sale of the property and are _________________ in Washington.

4. List the provisions that should be included in any listing agreement.

   1. ____
   2. ____
   3. ____
   4. ____
   5. ____
   6. ____
   7. ____

5. Salespersons working for the broker (are / are not) subject to the provisions of the agreement between broker and seller.

Exercise 9D

1. Most listing forms extend the agreement through the ____________ date if the seller signs a purchase and sale agreement.

2. A multiple listing provision sometimes stipulates that the ___________ agent will receive a portion of the listing agent's __________________.

3. Most MLS forms provide for access to the property by means of a _____________.

Exercise 9E

1. A printed listing agreement with the commission amount printed on it in advance would violate __________________ laws.

2. What is the reason for including an extender clause in a listing agreement?

   ____

3. A seller's liability to pay a commission under an extender clause usually depends on whether the broker's marketing activities had any impact on the sale. Describe the two classes of buyers who are commonly covered by extender clauses.

   1. ____
   2. ____

4. In order to give the seller notice that a sale to a certain buyer during the extender period will incur liability for a commission, the listing agreement may require the broker to give the seller ____.

5. Under the terms of most exclusive right to sell listings, the broker is entitled to a commission if any of three events occurs:

   1. ____
   2. ____
   3. ____

Exercise 9F

1. The typical listing agreement prohibits the seller from entering into an option to purchase or a ______________ agreement.

2. If a seller turns down an offer that matches the terms of the listing agreement, the seller is liable for the __________________.

3. Match the type of provision with the appropriate description:

___ seller's warranties	a. provides the maximum a seller will pay toward discount points and similar cost
___ FHA/VA loan costs	b. provides that seller will indemnify broker for losses arising from incorrect or incomplete information from seller
___ hold harmless agreement	c. usually includes statement that seller has right to sell the property

4. An attorney's fees provision provides that attorney's fees will be paid by the ______________ party to a lawsuit.

5. The property information form is a disclosure form completed by the ____________.

Exercise 9G

1. Circle any of the following who should sign a listing agreement:
   a. seller
   b. seller's spouse
   c. broker
   d. co-owners

2. It is (optional / required) for the agent to give the seller a copy of the listing agreement when it is signed.

3. When a salesperson takes a listing, how should he or she sign the listing agreement form?

____

Exercise 9H

1. Under Washington law, a seller is required to provide the buyer with a property disclosure statement if the property is ____________________ ____________________. The statement must be given to the buyer within ______________ after the purchase and sale agreement is executed, unless ____ or ____.
The buyer has the right to rescind the purchase and sale contract within ________________________ of receipt of the disclosure statement.

2. Indicate whether each of the following statements is true or false.

   The property disclosure statement becomes a part of the contract between the buyer and the seller. T F

   The seller is liable for any inaccuracies in a property disclosure statement. T F

   The broker is liable for any inaccuracies in a property disclosure statement. T F

   The buyer's right to rescind the contract after receipt of the disclosure statement does not depend on the contents of the disclosure statement. T F

3. What happens if the seller fails to provide a property disclosure statement to the buyer by the required deadline?

____

4. If new information comes to light after the seller has provided a property disclosure to the buyer, the seller has two options. What are they?

   1. ______________________________

   2. ______________________________

5. A seller has provided the required property disclosure statement to the buyer, and the buyer has accepted the statement. After closing, but before the buyer takes possession of the property, the seller discovers that there is a problem with the septic system. This problem was not disclosed on the property disclosure statement. Indicate whether each of the following statements is true or false.

   Since the sale has already closed, the property disclosure law is no longer relevant.
   T F

   The buyer may rescind the transaction within 3 days of learning about the problem with the septic system. T F

   The buyer may rescind the transaction at any time up to the date of possession.
   T F

Lesson 9: Workbook Quiz Questions

1. A listing agreement is a contract between a seller and a:

   a. broker
   b. salesperson
   c. multiple listing association
   d. buyer

2. The circumstances under which the seller will be required to pay the broker a commission are determined by:

   a. MLS rules
   b. the terms of the listing agreement
   c. the terms of the purchase and sale agreement
   d. the Department of Licensing

3. A broker's commission is usually:

   a. a percentage of the property's listing price
   b. a percentage of the property's appraised value
   c. a percentage of the property's sales price
   d. a flat fee based on the anticipated difficulty of selling the property

4. A broker cannot successfully sue a seller for a commission unless:

   a. they had a written listing agreement
   b. the broker was properly licensed at the time the brokerage services were provided
   c. the broker has fulfilled the terms of the listing agreement
   d. All of the above

5. A buyer is considered "ready and willing" to buy if he or she:

   a. makes an offer that meets the seller's stated terms
   b. makes any reasonable offer to purchase
   c. offers to pay at least the appraised value of the property
   d. makes an earnest money deposit

6. A "no sale, no commission" provision in a listing agreement:

   a. would make the broker's commission payable only if the buyer signs a purchase and sale agreement
   b. would make the broker's commission payable only if the transaction actually closes
   c. is included in most of the standard forms used in Washington
   d. is unenforceable

7. A buyer makes an offer that matches the seller's terms set forth in the listing agreement, but the seller decides not to accept the offer after all. Under the terms of most listing agreements, the broker is:

   a. entitled to keep the earnest money deposit
   b. required to refund the commission to the seller
   c. entitled to the commission anyway
   d. not entitled to any payment

8. When a buyer makes an offer on terms other than those set forth in the listing agreement:

    a. the broker should refuse to present it to the seller
    b. the seller is liable for the broker's commission whether he or she accepts the offer or not
    c. the seller can accept the offer without becoming liable for the broker's commission
    d. the seller can turn down the offer without becoming liable for the broker's commission

9. If a seller accepts a buyer's offer, as a general rule the seller is:

    a. required to pay the broker's commission whether or not the offer matched the terms set forth in the listing agreement
    b. only required to pay the broker's commission if the offer did not match the terms set forth in the listing agreement
    c. only required to pay the broker's commission if the offer matched the terms set forth in the listing agreement
    d. not required to pay the broker's commission, whether or not the offer matched the terms set forth in the listing agreement

10. A ready and willing buyer is considered "able" to buy only if he or she has:

    a. enough cash to buy the property on the agreed terms
    b. the capacity to contract and the financial ability to complete the purchase
    c. obtained a firm loan commitment from a mortgage broker or institutional lender
    d. prequalified for a loan from a reputable institutional lender

11. When a transaction fails to close, the broker is legally entitled to the commission:

    a. unless the seller and the buyer mutually agreed to terminate the transaction
    b. only if the buyer was the procuring cause
    c. if the failure to close was the seller's fault
    d. All of the above

12. The three basic types of listing agreements are:

    a. exclusive agency, net, multiple
    b. open, exclusive right to sell, net
    c. open, exclusive, multiple
    d. open, exclusive agency, exclusive right to sell

13. Under an open listing agreement, the seller is obligated to pay the broker a commission:

    a. only if the broker was the procuring cause of the sale
    b. whether or not a ready, willing, and able buyer is found during the listing period
    c. unless the seller found the buyer on his or her own
    d. no matter who found the buyer

14. A seller signs an open listing agreement with Broker A, and then immediately signs another open listing agreement with Broker B. If the property is sold before either listing expires, and Broker B is the procuring cause of the sale:
    a. the seller is required to pay the full commission to Broker A as well as to Broker B
    b. Broker A will not be compensated for his or her efforts
    c. Broker A and Broker B will each receive half of the agreed commission
    d. Broker A can sue the seller for breach of contract

15. An open listing is also called:
    a. an exclusive agency listing
    b. a multiple listing
    c. a non-exclusive listing
    d. a net listing

16. Open listings are:
    a. generally used only when a broker is unwilling to execute a net listing agreement
    b. illegal in Washington
    c. standard for residential property in Washington
    d. generally used only when a seller is unwilling to execute an exclusive listing agreement

17. With an exclusive agency listing, the seller:
    a. only lists the property with one broker, but retains the right to sell the property by him or herself without being obligated to pay the broker's commission
    b. can list the property with several brokers, but only one of the brokers is considered the seller's agent
    c. is only allowed to list the property with the procuring cause of the sale
    d. can list the property with several brokers, but is only obligated to pay a commission to the procuring cause

18. Under an exclusive right to sell listing, the broker is entitled to a commission:
    a. whether or not the property sells during the listing term
    b. if the property sells during the listing term, regardless of who finds the buyer
    c. only if he or she is the procuring cause of the sale
    d. unless the seller finds a buyer without the broker's help

19. The type of listing agreement that is most commonly used, and which provides the most protection for the broker, is:
    a. the double net listing
    b. the exclusive agency listing
    c. the exclusive right to sell listing
    d. the open listing

20. A seller authorizes a broker to actually sell the property (that is, to enter into a binding contract with a buyer) under the terms of a typical:
    a. exclusive right to sell listing agreement
    b. open listing agreement
    c. net listing agreement
    d. None of the above

21. Because a listing agreement is not enforceable in Washington unless it fixes the broker's compensation at a set rate or set amount, brokers here are not allowed to use:
    a. net listings
    b. keyboxes
    c. due diligence
    d. multiple listing services

22. If a broker submits an exclusive listing to a multiple listing service:
    a. the MLS is entitled to 50% of any commission earned on the listing
    b. the listing broker will share the commission if a cooperating broker from the MLS is the procuring cause of the sale
    c. all cooperating brokers from the MLS represent the seller
    d. All of the above

23. When a seller lists property with a broker, the broker's commission rate:
    a. must not be less than the minimum rate allowed by MLS rules
    b. cannot exceed the maximum rate allowed by law (10%)
    c. must be negotiable between the seller and the broker
    d. should be pre-printed in the listing form, not written or typed into a blank on the form

24. Many listing agreement forms provide that if the seller signs a purchase and sale agreement during the listing period:
    a. the listing is terminated immediately
    b. the buyer will pay half the broker's commission
    c. the broker will accept half the earnest money in lieu of the agreed commission
    d. the listing period is extended to the date set for closing the transaction

25. The listing agreement provides that if the seller sells the property within six months after the agreement expires to anyone who first learned of the property through the broker, the seller will be required to pay the broker's commission. This type of provision is called:
    a. an extender clause or safety clause
    b. a warranty clause or option provision
    c. an automatic renewal clause or holdover clause
    d. an antitrust clause or due diligence provision

Purchase and Sale Agreements

Exercise 10A

1. A purchase and sale agreement can also be called (circle all that are correct):
   a. a listing contract
   b. a purchase agreement
   c. a deposit receipt
   d. an earnest money agreement

2. A binding contract requires offer and acceptance. Circle the action below that constitutes a contract offer.
   a. A seller signs a listing agreement with a broker, putting her house on the market for $85,000.
   b. A buyer signs a purchase and sale agreement form, offering to buy the house for $80,000.

3. A purchase and sale agreement is required to be in writing under which of the following?
   a. The statute of frauds
   b. Contract evidence rule
   c. Rule of offer and acceptance
   d. Agency rules

4. Consideration in a purchase and sale agreement consists of two main promises. What are they?
   1. ______________________________
   2. ______________________________

5. True or false? A purchase and sale agreement is a binding contract only after the sale has closed. T F

6. A real estate agent can legally prepare a purchase and sale agreement:
   a. because a standard form is not a contract
   b. because of a limited exception to the rule that only an attorney can write a contract for others
   c. because the agent is not personally involved in the contract
   d. because an agent automatically has power of attorney for his or her clients

Exercise 10B

1. When the buyer is assuming the seller's mortgage, what portion of the mortgage is included in the purchase price? ____________

2. True or false? As the seller's agent, a real estate agent should not draw the buyer's attention to items such as light fixtures and appliances that are excluded from the sale. T F

3. What are the consequences if the property description in a purchase and sale agreement is inadequate?

   ____

4. If there is not enough space to enter the full property description on a preprinted form, what should the agent do?

   ____

5. Indicate whether each of the following statements is true or false.

   Any attachments to a purchase and sale agreement should be initialed by both the buyer and the seller. T F

   In a purchase and sale agreement, it is not necessary to state that the buyer's earnest money will be applied to the purchase price, since everyone knows this is common practice. T F

   If there is any doubt as to whether an item is included in the sale, the agreement should list the item and state whether or not it is included. T F

6. Unless otherwise agreed by the buyer and the seller, all items that are legally classified as ______________ are included in the sale of the real estate.

Exercise 10C

1. Match the following terms:

___ financing	a. postpones the closing date
___ closing	b. a prime consideration in determining a closing date
___ attached legal description	c. deals with the issue of fixtures
___ earnest money deposit	d. a date for this event must be set forth in the purchase and sale agreement
___ included items provision	e. purchase and sale agreement should state if this is to be applied to the price
___ extension agreement	f. needs to be initialed by buyer and seller

2. The agent should usually consult a ____________ to determine a suitable closing date.

3. Through no fault of either party, it appears that a sale will not close by the scheduled date. In such a case:
   a. the parties must terminate the purchase and sale agreement immediately
   b. the parties must split the closing costs and enter into a new agreement
   c. the parties can change the closing date in a written extension agreement
   d. the seller must rent to the buyer until closing can take place

4. The type of deed most commonly called for by purchase and sale agreement forms is a ______________________________ deed.

5. A ______________________________ clause, which appears in most purchase and sale agreements, means that failure to meet a deadline is a breach of the contract.

Exercise 10D

1. Purchase and sale agreements often specify which of the following items as liquidated damages?
   a. All fixtures not otherwise excluded
   b. Earnest money deposit
   c. Attorney's fees
   d. One-half of the broker's commission

2. True or false? Washington law limits liquidated damages to five percent of the earnest money deposit. T F

3. Washington law requires a real estate agent to disclose to the buyer and seller in writing which party he or she represents in the transaction. This information is usually included in the ______________________________ in a separate provision.

4. When is a selling agent required to make an agency disclosure?

   to the seller ______________________________

   to the buyer ______________________________

Exercise 10E

1. The reason for requiring spouses to sign purchase and sale agreements is to deal with the issue of ____________________ property.

2. Who should sign the receipt for the earnest money?

   ____

3. If the earnest money is in the form of a promissory note, the agent should: (circle all that apply)
   a. refuse to present the offer to the seller
   b. specify in the purchase offer that the earnest money is a promissory note
   c. place the note in the agent's trust account
   d. get the approval of his or her broker before accepting the note

4. Indicate whether each of the following statements is true or false.

   An agent may hold an earnest money check uncashed after the seller accepts the offer. T F

   All earnest money checks should be delivered to the closing agent without delay. T F

   An earnest money deposit must be at least $1,000 or 5% of the offering price, whichever is less. T F

   For an agent to suggest an amount for the earnest money deposit is a violation of the license law. T F

5. When does a purchase and sale agreement become a binding contract? (Circle all that apply.)

   a. When the seller signs the agreement
   b. When the seller's acceptance of the buyer's offer is communicated to the buyer
   c. When the buyer's acceptance of the seller's counteroffer is communicated to the seller
   d. When the seller's counteroffer is communicated to the buyer

---

Exercise 10F

1. The most common contingency clause is a ________________ contingency.

2. If a contingency is not met, the buyer ordinarily is entitled to receive a refund of the earnest money as long as there was a ________________ effort to fulfill the condition.

3. True or false? If possible, an agent should draft a contingency clause rather than using a contingency addendum form. T F

4. Any contingency clause should contain four basic elements:

   1. ________________________________
   2. ________________________________
   3. ________________________________
   4. ________________________________

5. Who is entitled to waive a contingency in a purchase and sale agreement?

   ____

Exercise 10G

1. To fulfill a/an __________ contingency, a seller must deliver a written appraisal valuing the property at no less than the agreed sales price.

2. The clause that enables a seller to keep the property on the market while waiting for a contingency to be met is known as a __________ clause.

3. Inspection contingency clauses should incorporate _______________ standards of fulfillment so that the buyer does not have total discretion as to whether or not inspection results are satisfactory.

4. The description of a financing contingency should include:
   1. ____________________________________
   2. ____________________________________
   3. ____________________________________
   4. ____________________________________
   5. ____________________________________

5. A buyer and seller enter a purchase and sale agreement on May 25. Closing is set for August 1. The sale is contingent on the sale of the buyer's current residence, and the agreement specifies that the buyer will have 90 days to sell the current residence or waive the contingency. What is wrong with this scenario?

   ____

Lesson 10: Workbook Quiz Questions

1. In most real estate transactions, the buyer is the:

   a. offeror
   b. offeree
   c. agent
   d. party responsible for setting a closing date

2. An offer to purchase real property:

   a. need not be in writing because it is only preliminary to a contract
   b. should be in writing because of the statute of frauds
   c. must be in writing because it is a contract
   d. should not be in writing until it is accepted

3. A binding contract exists:

   a. as soon as the buyer signs the purchase and sale agreement form
   b. when the agent receives the signed form from the buyer
   c. after the seller signs the form signed by the buyer and returns it to the buyer
   d. once the earnest money has been received by the agent

4. A contract for the purchase and sale of real estate is formed by:

   a. offer and counteroffer
   b. offer and consideration
   c. offer and delivery
   d. offer and acceptance

5. The prohibition against the unauthorized practice of law prohibits a real estate agent from:

   a. completing a purchase and sale agreement form for a buyer
   b. accepting an earnest money deposit
   c. completing a purchase and sale agreement form for a seller
   d. completing a purchase and sale agreement form for a transaction in which the agent is not representing either party

6. If the provisions of the purchase and sale form being used do not adequately cover the transaction an agent is handling, the agent may:

   a. attach a simple addendum
   b. rewrite the unsuitable provisions
   c. write a new agreement that covers the transaction
   d. None of the above

7. When completing a purchase and sale agreement form, a real estate agent must meet the same standard of care as:

   a. an attorney
   b. a private individual acting in his or her own best interest
   c. the seller
   d. the offeror

8. Which of the following items does not need to be included in a purchase and sale agreement?

   a. Adequate description of the property
   b. Copy of the deed
   c. Method of payment
   d. Closing date

9. If the full legal description of a property is too long to fit on the form, the agent should:
   a. use the street address instead
   b. give as much of the description as will fit in the space provided
   c. attach a separate sheet with the full description
   d. insert a reference to the recorder's office where the deed is on file

10. If the buyer will assume the seller's mortgage balance of $50,000 and pay the seller $85,000 cash at closing, the agent should fill in the space provided for purchase price as follows:
    a. $85,000
    b. $50,000
    c. $35,000
    d. $135,000

11. An addendum listing those items to be excluded from the sale should be:
    a. signed by the buyer
    b. filed with the Department of Licensing
    c. recorded in the county in which the property is located
    d. presented to the buyer at closing

12. The date on which the seller receives the proceeds of the sale, the deed is delivered to the buyer, and all documents are recorded is called the:
    a. closing date
    b. termination date
    c. transfer of possession
    d. date of acceptance

13. A written extension agreement between buyer and seller serves to:
    a. terminate the existing purchase and sale agreement
    b. defer the closing date
    c. invalidate the listing agreement
    d. None of the above

14. Transfer of possession:
    a. cannot occur before closing
    b. must occur after closing
    c. normally takes place at closing
    d. is the same as closing

15. If the seller is aware of zoning or building code violations on the property:
    a. the purchase and sale agreement is invalid
    b. the agent is acting with apparent authority only
    c. the title cannot be transferred
    d. they should be listed in the purchase and sale agreement

16. The type of deed specified in most purchase and sale agreement forms is a:
    a. special warranty deed
    b. general warranty deed
    c. tax deed
    d. bargain and sale deed

17. If a purchase and sale agreement provides that time is of the essence:
    a. timely performance is considered an essential term of the agreement
    b. failure to meet any deadline is a breach of the contract
    c. both buyer and seller are required to meet all deadlines in the agreement
    d. All of the above

18. The remedy of liquidated damages:
    a. is only available if provided by contract
    b. is available if there is an earnest money deposit exceeding 5 of the purchase price
    c. is rarely provided for in purchase and sale agreements
    d. only applies if a financial loss can be shown

19. An earnest money deposit:

    a. can be any amount the parties agree upon
    b. may not be paid in cash
    c. must be deposited in a trust account immediately upon receipt
    d. must be at least 5% of the sales price

20. If a buyer makes an offer to purchase a house and sets no deadline for the seller's acceptance:

    a. the seller can accept at any time and create a binding contract
    b. the offer is invalid
    c. the offer expires 30 days from delivery
    d. the offer terminates if not accepted within a reasonable time

21. The effect of a counteroffer is to:

    a. extend the deadline for acceptance of the original offer
    b. revise the existing contract to purchase
    c. terminate the offer
    d. create a new, binding contract

22. The buyer's offer to purchase was conditioned on satisfactory results of a geological inspection. After the seller accepted the offer, the buyer notified her that he had decided the inspection was unnecessary after all. In this situation:

    a. the seller can sue for breach of contract
    b. the buyer must pay the cost of an inspection to the seller
    c. the buyer forfeits his earnest money
    d. the seller is bound by the agreement whether or not the inspection is performed

23. Despite a good faith effort, the buyer was unable to obtain financing on the terms spelled out in the contingency clause. As a result:

    a. the seller is entitled to damages
    b. the earnest money is forfeited
    c. the purchase and sale agreement terminates and the earnest money is refunded
    d. new financing terms must be specified

24. A bump clause:

    a. permits a seller to keep the property on the market pending fulfillment of a contingency
    b. allows a VA purchaser to make up the difference between the appraisal price and the purchase price
    c. can only be exercised with the permission of the first buyer
    d. prohibits the seller from accepting contingent offers

25. Christine conditioned her offer to purchase a new home on the sale of her current home. She receives a satisfactory offer, which she accepts. The contingency:

    a. is satisfied
    b. is satisfied if the contingency clause stated that Christine's acceptance of an offer fulfilled the contingency
    c. is not satisfied until the closing date for the sale of Christine's current home
    d. is not satisfied until the buyer of Christine's current home obtains financing

Lesson 11

Listing and Selling Practices

Exercise 11A

1. List the five methods commonly used by real estate agents to obtain listings.
   1. ______________________________
   2. ______________________________
   3. ______________________________
   4. ______________________________
   5. ______________________________

2. List three potential sources from which real estate agents may obtain referrals.
   1. ______________________________
   2. ______________________________
   3. ______________________________

3. When selecting an area to farm for listings, a real estate agent should be concerned with three factors:
   1. ______________________________
   2. ______________________________
   3. ______________________________

4. Indicate whether each of the following statements is true or false.

   A good way to obtain listings is to approach sellers whose property is already listed with another broker and attempt to get them to switch brokers. T F

   Cold calling is most effective if the agent selects homeowners at random. T F

   Obtaining listings by cold calling or farming requires a significant amount of time and effort. T F

5. If an agent has a prospective buyer for a property that is for sale by owner, the agent may be able to earn a commission by convincing the seller to sign a ______________________________.

Exercise 11B

1. The purpose of a competitive market analysis is to ________________________ ______________________________.

2. In a competitive market analysis, the ceiling of values in the market is illustrated by ____________________________________, and the best indication of current market values is illustrated by ______________________________ ______________.

3. What is the reason for using a "net proceeds to seller" form in a listing presentation?

   ____

4. Indicate whether each of the following statements is true or false.

   Prior to making a listing presentation, a real estate agent should personally inspect the owner's property and the neighborhood. T F

   If an agent thinks the seller's asking price is too high, the best course of action is to refuse to take the listing. T F

   Real estate agents often recommend that the seller set the listing price at a figure that is somewhat higher than the expected selling price, in order to leave room for negotiation with potential buyers. T F

Exercise 11C

1. The most important form of advertising for a listed property is ________________________________.

2. List the five "trigger" terms that trigger the disclosure requirements of the Truth in Lending Act.

   1. ______________________
   2. ______________________
   3. ______________________
   4. ______________________
   5. ______________________

3. Why do real estate agents hold open houses, when the odds of finding a buyer in this manner are extremely low?

   ____

4. Indicate whether each of the following statements is true or false.

   An advertisement for a listed property must always state the name of the listing broker, even if the brokerage is a franchise. T F

   Advertising a listed property is a good way to attract buyers for other listed properties that are not advertised. T F

   At an open house, the sellers should always be present to answer any questions and to help show the property. T F

5. What are the reasons for having guests sign a guest log at an open house?

   ____

Exercise 11D

1. The process of determining how much a buyer can afford to pay for a home is called ______________________.

2. Match the type of buyer on the left with the type of property on the right.

___ first-time buyer	a. easily maintained homes with low monthly payments
___ trade-up buyer	b. smaller, low-cost homes
___ empty-nester	c. smaller homes, without regard to cost
___ retiree	d. larger, more expensive homes

3. Indicate whether each of the following statements is true or false.

   An agent should never show a buyer a home that the agent has not previewed. T F

   When showing a home, it is important to stay close to the buyers at all times. T F

   The more homes an agent can show to a prospect at one time, the better the chances of making a sale. T F

4. When an agent is assigned to ________________, the agent is responsible for handling all phone calls and walk-in customers at the office for a specified time period.

5. List three ways that agents can identify or attract potential buyers.

   1. ____
   2. ____
   3. ____

Exercise 11E

1. The most common objections sellers have upon receipt of an initial offer from a buyer concern the ________________, the ________________, the ________________ and the ________________.

2. When a buyer gives the agent a check for an earnest money deposit along with the buyer's offer, how does the agent usually handle the earnest money?

   ____

3. At what point should an agent give the parties copies of documents they have signed?
   a. At the time the documents are signed
   b. When the seller accepts the buyer's offer
   c. At least 3 days before the closing date

4. Indicate whether each of the following statements is true or false.

   When a cooperating agent receives an offer from a buyer, the offer should be given to the listing agent to present to the seller. T F

   It is a good idea to meet customers at the office before taking them to view properties that are for sale. T F

   When presenting an offer to a seller, it is usually best to deal with the negative aspects of the offer first, so the seller can concentrate on the positive side. T F

5. In order to reduce the risk of theft during an open house or when a property is shown to prospects, an agent should advise the seller to:
   a. install an alarm system
   b. remove any small valuable items from the premises
   c. not allow the house to be shown unless the seller is present
   d. purchase additional theft insurance

Lesson 11: Workbook Quiz Questions

1. When choosing an area to farm for listings, and agent should be concerned about:
   a. the rate of turnover in the area
   b. the diversity of homes in the area
   c. the agent's affinity for the area
   d. All of the above

2. An expired listing is probably not a good prospect for an agent if:
   a. the previous listing price was too high
   b. the property requires minor repairs to improve its marketability
   c. the sellers are not motivated
   d. the previous listing was held by a cooperating broker

3. Which of the following methods of obtaining listings would likely result in the highest rate of success?
   a. Cold calling
   b. Farming
   c. Contacting sellers whose listings have expired
   d. Referrals

4. An agent is most likely to obtain a listing for a "for sale by owner" property if:
   a. the agent can convince the seller that the agent can sell the property faster and for a higher price
   b. the seller has spent substantial amounts of money on marketing the property without success
   c. the property has been on the market for at least 90 days
   d. the agent promises to submit the property to a multiple listing service

5. When making a listing presentation to a seller, an agent should:
   a. assure the seller that the property can be sold within the standard 90 day listing term
   b. disclose to the seller that the listing price will be established by the broker for best results
   c. be well prepared and act professionally, since the seller will likely be considering listing with other firms as well
   d. All of the above

6. A competitive market analysis serves all of the following purposes, except:
   a. makes clear to the seller that the agent's estimate of the value of the seller's property is based on facts, not personal opinion
   b. helps the agent present market information to the seller in an orderly, easily understood manner
   c. helps the seller make a decision on a realistic listing price
   d. guarantees that the property will be sold if the seller accepts the agent's recommended list price

7. Which of the following would not ordinarily be included in a competitive market analysis?
   a. Information about homes that have sold recently
   b. Information about homes that are similar to the seller's home but are not currently listed for sale
   c. Information about homes that are currently listed for sale in the seller's neighborhood
   d. Information about homes that were recently listed for sale, but whose listings have expired

8. When setting a realistic listing price, the upper limit of the price range would be indicated by:
   a. the listing prices of expired listings for similar properties
   b. the listing prices of similar properties that are currently for sale in the market
   c. the listing prices of similar properties that have recently been sold
   d. the selling prices of similar properties that have recently been sold

9. A "net proceeds to seller" form is used to:
   a. help the seller set a realistic listing price
   b. inform the seller of the commission amount
   c. inform the seller of the amount he or she can expect to receive from the sale after paying the commission and other closing costs
   d. inform the seller of the property's true market value

10. Once an agent has obtained a listing, he or she should:
    a. try to convince the seller to leave town for a few weeks to make it easier to show the property
    b. encourage the seller to make minor repairs that will improve the marketability of the property
    c. wait until the seller repaints the home before showing it to any prospects
    d. order an appraisal to verify that the listing price is not too high

11. In order to prepare a listed property for showing to prospects, the agent should recommend that the seller do all of the following except:
    a. repaint the interior walls in bright colors, which makes the rooms seem larger
    b. remove any old vehicles from the property
    c. prune the trees and shrubs
    d. replace outdated carpets and wallpaper

12. The most important form of advertising for a listed property is usually:
    a. the "For Sale" sign posted at the property and showing the name of the brokerage
    b. printed fliers that can be distributed to buyers who inquire about the property
    c. submitting the listing to a multiple listing service
    d. classified ads in local newspapers

13. A newspaper advertisement for a listed property should always include:
    a. the name of the listing broker
    b. the name of the listing salesperson
    c. the terms of any seller financing that is available
    d. All of the above

14. Which of the following phrases in an advertisement would trigger the disclosure requirements of the Truth in Lending Act?
    a. "VA and FHA financing available"
    b. "10% down, easy terms"
    c. "No downpayment required"
    d. "Assume 10% annual percentage rate loan"

15. If an advertisement triggers the disclosure requirements of the Truth in Lending Act, the ad must disclose all of the following except:
    a. the amount of the downpayment
    b. the amount of the closing costs
    c. the terms of repayment of the financing
    d. the annual percentage rate of the financing

16. The biggest advantage of holding an open house for a listed property is:
    a. the property is exposed to many potential buyers who otherwise would not take the time to view it
    b. the agent can contact many prospective buyers and sellers who are potential customers or clients
    c. the sellers are more likely to make an effort to spruce up the property if they know there will be an open house
    d. the agent saves a tremendous amount of time because she doesn't have to visit the property separately with each potential buyer

17. When an agent is holding an open house and a customer refuses to sign in on the guest register, the agent should:
    a. refuse to allow the customer to view the property
    b. insist on seeing a photo ID before allowing the customer to view the property
    c. threaten to call the police if the customer does not leave immediately
    d. allow the customer to view the property unless the seller has given specific instructions to the contrary

18. The term "floor duty" refers to:
    a. the practice of assigning one agent in an office to handle all phone calls and walk-in inquiries for the office during a specified time period
    b. the practice of assigning office maintenance to different agents on a rotating basis
    c. the requirement that an agent spend a minimum amount of time in the broker's office each day
    d. None of the above

19. Agent's should prequalify potential customers in order to determine:
    a. whether the customer seriously intends to buy a house or is just shopping around
    b. whether the customer is interested in any of the properties listed in-house at the agent's firm
    c. whether or not to enter into a buyer agency agreement with the customer to avoid conflicts of interest
    d. how much the customer can realistically afford to spend on a house

20. When showing properties to a customer, an agent should:
    a. always show at least six different properties so the customer can make an informed choice
    b. only show homes the customer can afford to buy
    c. show the customer any home that meets the customer's needs, regardless of price
    d. None of the above

21. If an agent presents an offer and the seller wants to make a counteroffer, the agent should:

    a. try to convince the seller to accept the original offer without changes
    b. refer the seller to an attorney to prepare the counteroffer
    c. advise the seller to make the desired changes on the contract form and initial them
    d. advise the seller to make the desired changes on a separate counteroffer form

22. An agent is required to give the buyer a copy of any documents signed by the buyer:

    a. at the time the seller accepts the buyer's offer
    b. at the time the buyer signs the documents
    c. at least 3 days before the closing date
    d. at least 10 days before the closing date

23. When arranging to show a property to a customer, it is best to:

    a. arrange to meet the customer at the property, in order to save time
    b. arrange to meet the customer at the agent's office
    c. call ahead to make sure that the seller will be home when the property is shown
    d. recommend that the customer drive by the property first to make sure he is really interested in it

24. As a safety precaution, agents should:

    a. arrange to check in with someone on a regular basis when they are showing properties
    b. make sure that a phone is available for emergencies during open houses
    c. work in pairs if possible during open houses and when showing properties
    d. All of the above

25. In most cases, the earnest money that accompanies a buyer's offer to purchase is:

    a. deposited immediately into the seller's bank account
    b. deposited immediately into escrow
    c. deposited immediately into the broker's account
    d. held uncashed by the broker pending acceptance by the seller of the buyer's offer

Real Estate Finance: Principles

Exercise 12A

1. List the Federal Reserve's main tools for implementing monetary policy.
   1. ____________________________________
   2. ____________________________________
   3. ____________________________________

2. Match the following terms:

___ open market operations	a. taxation, spending, and debt management
___ federal deficit	b. efforts to control money supply and interest rates
___ monetary policy	c. charged to member banks on loans from Fed
___ discount rate	d. when the Fed buys and sells government securities
___ fiscal policy	e. shortfall that results when spending exceeds revenues

3. In order to stimulate the economy, the Fed might decide to increase the money supply. It could increase the money supply by (circle all that are correct):
   a. buying government securities
   b. lowering reserve requirements
   c. raising the discount rate
   d. increasing the federal deficit

4. Lower interest rates tend to (dampen / stimulate) the economy.

5. The agency that manages the national debt is ______________________. This agency's activities affect the real estate finance market because ____________ ______________________________.

Exercise 12B

1. The Garcias just borrowed $132,000 from a local bank to finance the purchase of their home. This transaction took place in the ______________ mortgage market.

2. The primary market is the one in which lenders __________ mortgage loans to ________________. The secondary market is the one in which lenders __________ mortgage loans to ________________.

3. A local lender that is running short of loan funds would be likely to ____________ ____________________________ in order to obtain more money to lend.

4. A mortgage loan generally cannot be sold on the secondary market unless the lender has complied with the _____________________________.

5. The original source of funds for the primary market is ______________________ ____________________.

Exercise 12C

1. Match the following terms:

___ real estate cycles	a. national market
___ primary market	b. supply and demand
___ uniform standards	c. buys mortgage loans
___ secondary market	d. set by secondary market agencies
___ Fannie Mae	e. local market

2. List the major government-sponsored secondary market agencies.
   1. ____________________
   2. ____________________
   3. ____________________

3. Indicate whether each of the following statements is true or false.

   The availability of funds in the primary mortgage market depends a great deal on the existence of the national secondary market. T F

   Uniform loan underwriting standards are critical to the operation of the secondary market. T F

   Fannie Mae is a private corporation that buys conventional loans. T F

4. The agency that provides government guarantees for securities based on pools of FHA and VA mortgages is ____________________.

5. The government department that oversees the activities of the major secondary market agencies is ____________________.

Exercise 12D

1. List the four main types of residential lenders in the primary market:
   1. ____________________
   2. ____________________
   3. ____________________
   4. ____________________

   Which of these types of lenders is not a depository institution?

   ____

2. FIRREA, a federal law passed in 1989, was the congressional response to the ____________________.

3. An intermediary that arranges and services loans on behalf of a large investor is called a ______________________________.

4. When a property seller extends credit to the buyer (instead of requiring full payment at closing), it is called ______________________________.

5. Indicate whether each of the following statements is true or false.

   A mortgage banker is someone who negotiates loans between lenders and borrowers for a commission. T F

   Credit unions are a major force in the primary mortgage market. T F

   Savings and loans have a much larger share of the residential finance market than commercial banks. T F

   There is wide variation among the different types of primary lenders in terms of their standards and procedures for making home loans. T F

Exercise 12E

1. Which of the following loans is covered by the Truth in Lending Act? (Circle all that are correct.)

   a. A $55,000 mortgage loan used for agricultural purposes

   b. A $20,000 home equity loan used to pay for college tuition

   c. A $120,000 mortgage loan from a savings bank, used to purchase a home

2. Which of the following is required to comply with the disclosure requirements of the Truth in Lending Act? (Circle all that are correct.)

   a. An institutional lender

   b. A seller offering seller financing

   c. A credit arranger

3. Match the following terms:

___ consumer loan	a. does not include appraisal fee
___ APR	b. higher than interest rate
___ disclosure statement	c. implements the Truth in Lending Act
___ total finance charge	d. provided within three days after application received
___ Regulation Z	e. personal, family, or household purposes

4. An advertisement for consumer credit can list the loan's ____________________ without triggering the Truth in Lending Act's full disclosure requirement.

5. If the Truth in Lending Act's full disclosure requirement is triggered, the lender is required to disclose:
   1. ______________________________
   2. ______________________________
   3. ______________________________
   4. ______________________________
   5. ______________________________
   6. ______________________________
   7. ______________________________
   8. ______________________________

Exercise 12F

1. Chambers loans money to Dunlop and has Dunlop sign a negotiable promissory note. Chambers can transfer her right to repayment to a third party by ______________________ the note.

2. The basic elements of a promissory note are:
    1. ______________________________
    2. ______________________________
    3. ______________________________
    4. ______________________________

3. A note in which none of the principal is due to be repaid until the end of the loan term is called ____________________.

4. What does the term "fully amortized" mean with respect to a promissory note?

____

5. Indicate whether each of the following statements is true or false.

    The borrower should always keep a signed copy of the promissory note. T F

    An interest only note is one that is partially amortized. T F

    Most promissory notes used in real estate financing are negotiable instruments. T F

    The maker of a promissory note is called the holder in due course. T F

Exercise 12G

1. Match the following terms:

___ security instrument	a. buys note from payee
___ negotiable instrument	b. interest-only loan
___ holder in due course	c. signs note
___ maker	d. promissory note
___ straight note	e. deed of trust

2. In regard to security instruments, Washington law follows:
    a. lien theory
    b. title theory

3. A real estate lender has a borrower sign a security instrument as well as a promissory note, because the security instrument gives the lender the right to __________ ______________________________ if the debt is not repaid.

4. Put each of the following terms under the appropriate heading shown below:

   payee

   maker

   mortgagee

   mortgagor

   trustor

   beneficiary

BORROWER	LENDER

5. Indicate whether each of the following statements is true or false.

   Most real estate loans in Washington are secured by mortgages. T F

   The main difference between a mortgage and a deed of trust is the method of foreclosure. T F

   A mortgage or deed of trust does not create an enforceable lien unless it is recorded. T F

Exercise 12H

1. After the Carters had missed four monthly mortgage payments, the lender demanded that they pay off the entire principal balance immediately. The provision in the loan documents that allowed the lender to do this is called a/an _______________ __________________ clause.

2. If a borrower sells the security property without paying off the mortgage, the purchaser can either ________________ the mortgage or else take title ______________________ the mortgage. However, if the mortgage contains a/an ________________________ clause, the lender can require the borrower to pay off the loan if the property is sold.

3. Which of the following is ordinarily included in the documents for a typical home purchase loan? (Circle all that are correct.)
   a. acceleration clause
   b. alienation clause
   c. lock-in clause
   d. subordination clause

4. What is the effect of a lock-in clause?

   ____

5. Indicate whether each of the following statements is true or false.

   An alienation clause prevents the borrower from selling the property without the lender's approval. T F

   A mortgage or deed of trust must contain an complete description of the security property. T F

   Residential loans almost always include a prepayment penalty. T F

Exercise 12I

1. Match the following terms:

___ alienation clause	a. secondary liability
___ assumption	b. prepayment not allowed
___ subordination clause	c. release of lien
___ lock-in clause	d. due-on-sale
___ satisfaction	e. lower lien priority

2. If the proceeds of the sheriff's sale are more than enough to pay off the loan and foreclosure costs, the excess amount belongs to the _______________. If the sale proceeds are not sufficient to pay off the loan, the mortgagee may be entitled to a _______________________________.

3. The redemption period before a sheriff's sale is called the period of ____________ __________________. The redemption period after a sheriff's sale is called the period of ____________________________.

4. The document used to release a mortgage lien is called ____________________ _______________. The document used to release a deed of trust lien is called ___________________________________.

5. Indicate whether each of the following statements is true or false.

   The purchaser at a sheriff's sale receives a sheriff's deed. T F

   The purchaser at a sheriff's sale does not receive title to the property until after the statutory redemption period. T F

   In Washington, a mortgagee can shorten the statutory redemption period by agreeing not to seek a deficiency judgment. T F

Exercise 12J

1. List the following terms under the appropriate headings shown below:
   a. non-judicial foreclosure
   b. judicial foreclosure
   c. statutory redemption
   d. cure and reinstatement
   e. trustee's sale
   f. sheriff's sale
   g. deficiency judgment
   h. power of sale clause

MORTGAGE	DEED OF TRUST

2. To prevent a deed of trust foreclosure, the borrower doesn't have to pay off the entire debt. Instead, he or she can cure the default and reinstate the loan by paying ____.

3. The deadline for reinstating a deed of trust loan by curing the default is ________ ____________________________.

4. What is the minimum length of time between a borrower's default and the resulting trustee's sale?

   ____

5. From a lender's perspective, a deed of trust has two significant advantages over a mortgage, and one significant disadvantage. What are they?

   Advantages: ____

   Disadvantage: ____

Exercise 12K

1. Match the following terms:

___ conventional loan		a.	seller extends credit to buyer
___ blanket mortgage		b.	lender receives a share of property's earnings
___ budget mortgage		c.	not insured by a government agency
___ purchase money mortgage		d.	lower lien priority
___ junior mortgage		e.	covers more than one parcel of property
___ participation mortgage		f.	monthly payment includes taxes and insurance

2. A construction loan is sometimes called a/an ______________ loan. When construction is completed, that loan is replaced with permanent financing, known as a ________________ loan.

3. Regarding wraparound financing, answer true or false for the following.

   The buyer assumes the underlying loan. T F

   The seller makes the payments on the underlying loan. T F

   A wraparound should not be arranged if the underlying loan has an alienation clause. T F

4. The term "purchase money mortgage" can have two different meanings:

   1. ____

   2. ____

5. Indicate whether each of the following statements is true or false.

   The interest rate on an open-end mortgage is usually a variable rate. T F

   Participation loans are commonly used to finance single-family residences. T F

   Most residential loans are secured by budget mortgages. T F

Exercise 12L

1. Dan Elmore is buying the Towners' property under a land contract.

   Elmore is the (vendor / vendee).

   Elmore has (legal title / equitable title) to the property.

   The Towners will deliver the deed to Elmore when he has ____________________ ____________________.

   If Elmore defaults on the contract, the Towners could pursue a special legal remedy that would not have been available to them if they'd used a mortgage instead of a land contract. This remedy is called ____________________.

2. List the three types of disbursement plans used in connection with construction loans:

   1. ____

   2. ____

   3. ____

3. When property is sold under a land contract, who is usually responsible for payment of the property taxes?

   ____

4. The vendee under a land contract must be given a minimum of ____________ in which to cure a default under the contract.

5. Indicate whether each of the following statements is true or false.

   In order for the vendor to be able to use the forfeiture remedy, the land contract must be recorded. T F

   The vendee may redeem the property within 90 days after the Declaration of Forfeiture is recorded. T F

   In order for the vendor to be able to use the forfeiture remedy, the land contract must contain a forfeiture clause. T F

Lesson 12: Workbook Quiz Questions

1. Government borrowing from private investors takes place when the Treasury:
   a. sells interest-bearing securities
   b. sells stock in private companies
   c. raises interest rates
   d. raises taxes on corporations

2. How many commercial banks are members of the Federal Reserve System?
   a. 12
   b. over 5,000
   c. 24
   d. 250

3. An increase in reserve requirements by the Federal Reserve System results in:
   a. more money in circulation
   b. lower interest rates
   c. a reduction in the amount of money banks have available to lend
   d. a higher federal deficit

4. The secondary market:
   a. moderates extremes in the real estate market
   b. involves the purchase and sale of home mortgage loans
   c. imposes uniform underwriting standards on loans
   d. All of the above

5. Primary market lenders include:
   a. FNMA and FHLMC
   b. FHA and VA
   c. GNMA
   d. banks, S&Ls, and mortgage companies

6. A commercial bank loans money to a homebuyer without following uniform underwriting standards. The bank:
   a. probably cannot sell the loan to Fannie Mae
   b. has violated the Truth in Lending Act
   c. may not foreclose the loan in the event of default
   d. is allowed to make the loan, provided that it obtains a blanket mortgage from the borrower

7. In 1989 Congress passed FIRREA in order to:
   a. reorganize the system for regulating S&Ls
   b. regulate residential mortgage hazard insurers
   c. deregulate savings and loan associations
   d. discourage thrifts from making residential loans

8. Which of the following does not engage in residential lending for individual home purchases?
   a. Commercial bank
   b. Real estate investment trust
   c. Savings bank
   d. Mortgage company

9. Which of the following loans comes under the provisions of the Truth in Lending Act?
   a. A $50,000 loan to ABC Corporation that is secured by real property
   b. A consumer loan of $5,000 to be paid off in three monthly installments with no interest
   c. A home equity loan for $50,000 that will be used to remodel the borrower's home
   d. None of the above

10. Which of the following must be disclosed under the Truth in Lending Act?
    a. APR
    b. Mortgage insurance premiums and discount points the borrower pays
    c. Loan payment schedule
    d. All of the above

11. Andrea borrows money from Trust Bank to purchase a house. She signs a promissory note in which she agrees to repay the loan. Andrea is called:
    a. the maker of the note
    b. the payee of the note
    c. the endorser on the note
    d. a holder in due course

12. Benjamin signs a note for $10,000 at 8% interest to be paid off in three years. His payments will be $800 a year during the loan term. At the end of three years, he will pay off the full $10,000. Benjamin has a:
    a. straight note
    b. amortized note
    c. partly amortized note
    d. budget note

13. Trust Bank is the payee on a note, which it endorses to New Bank. New Bank is called a:
    a. grantor
    b. holder in due course
    c. vendor
    d. trustee

14. In State X, a lender receives naked title when it obtains a security interest in real estate. State X subscribes to the:
    a. lien theory
    b. hypothecation theory
    c. title theory
    d. security interest theory

15. One difference between a mortgage and a deed of trust is that:
    a. a deed of trust creates a security interest in real property
    b. in a lien theory state, a mortgage does not actually transfer title to the mortgagee
    c. a deed of trust may contain an alienation clause
    d. foreclosure is easier with a deed of trust

16. Most mortgages and deeds of trust contain provisions relating to all of the following except:
    a. taxes and insurance
    b. forfeiture
    c. acceleration
    d. property maintenance

17. An alienation clause:
    a. places no restrictions on loan assumption
    b. prohibits sale of the subject property
    c. provides for full payment of the loan in case of default
    d. provides for acceleration of the loan if the property is sold

18. A novation occurs:
    a. with the lender's approval
    b. without the lender's approval
    c. when the original borrower continues to be liable
    d. as an exception to the usual rule that "first in time is first in right"

19. A provision that reverses the normal priority of liens is known as a:
    a. subordination clause
    b. defeasance clause
    c. reconveyance clause
    d. lock-in clause

20. Which of the following applies to foreclosure under a deed of trust?
    a. Period of equitable redemption
    b. Deficiency judgment
    c. Statutory redemption period
    d. Non-judicial foreclosure

21. Which of the following terms concerns the issue of lien priority?
    a. Budget mortgage
    b. Open-end mortgage
    c. Senior mortgage
    d. Blanket mortgage

22. Most residential mortgages are:
    a. blanket mortgages
    b. open-end mortgages
    c. wraparound mortgages
    d. budget mortgages

23. An impound account is also known as a:
    a. forfeiture account
    b. partial reconveyance account
    c. reserve account
    d. default account

24. Under the terms of a typical land contract:
    a. the vendor holds title until the vendee has paid the full price
    b. the vendor usually pays property taxes and insurance
    c. foreclosure is the vendor's primary remedy
    d. the vendor must take the vendee to court in order to terminate the contract

25. Under the forfeiture remedy in a land contract:
    a. the vendor may sue for a deficiency judgment if the property is worth less than the amount still owed
    b. the vendor can retain all payments made by the vendee
    c. after a Notice of Intent to Forfeit has been filed, the vendee must pay off the entire debt to avoid forfeiture
    d. the vendee can redeem within 10 days after the Declaration of Forfeiture has been filed

Lesson 13

Real Estate Finance: Loan Underwriting

Exercise 13A

1. In evaluating a mortgage loan application, a loan underwriter tries to answer two fundamental questions: whether the applicant could be expected to make the loan payments as agreed, and whether the property ____________________________

   ____.

2. List the three basic elements an underwriter considers in evaluating a loan applicant's financial situation:

   1. ______________________________
   2. ______________________________
   3. ______________________________

3. An underwriter is concerned with the _______________, _______________, and _______________ of a loan applicant's income.

4. Underwriting standards generally call for a history of at least ___________ of continuous employment in the same line of work.

5. Indicate whether each of the following statements is true or false.

   Wages from part-time work may not be considered as part of a borrower's stable monthly income. T F

   Stable monthly income is defined as income that meets the lender's standards of quantity and quality. T F

   Changing jobs or employers is not always a negative factor in an underwriting evaluation. T F

Exercise 13B

1. Describe the two methods that lenders use to verify a loan applicant's employment income.

   1. ______________________________

   2. ______________________________

2. List three factors that a lender would consider in evaluating income in the form of alimony or spousal maintenance.

   1. ______________________________

   2. ______________________________

   3. ______________________________

3. Most loan programs will not include child support payments in the applicant's stable monthly income if the child is over the age of _____.

4. Indicate whether each of the following statements is true or false.

   Even if rental income is verified, lenders often exclude a percentage of the income from the applicant's stable monthly income. T F

   Income in the form of food stamps may be used to qualify for a loan. T F

   Most lenders are more concerned with the quality of an applicant's income than its durability. T F

5. If a loan applicant is relying on self-employment income to qualify for a loan, the lender will usually ask to see ______________________________.

Exercise 13C

1. An underwriter considers income from certain sources acceptable (so that it can be counted as part of stable monthly income) and income from other sources unacceptable. List the following types of income under the appropriate heading shown below.

   a. Wages from a permanent part-time job

   b. Salary from a permanent full-time job

   c. Wages from a temporary job

   d. Self-employment income from a new business

   e. Social security benefits

   f. Pension payments

   g. Unemployment compensation

   h. Child support for a six-year-old child

Usually Acceptable	Usually Unacceptable

2. What is the definition of stable monthly income?

   ____

3. Under what circumstances would income from temporary employment be considered acceptable as part of an applicant's stable monthly income?

   ____

4. Income from a member of the applicant's family who lives with the applicant may be counted towards the applicant's stable monthly income if the family member is (circle all that apply):

   a. the applicant's spouse

   b. the applicant's parent

   c. the applicant's child

5. True or false? Income from investments such as stocks and bonds is not included in stable monthly income because it is not reliable due to market fluctuations.

   T F

Exercise 13D

1. Susan Rashid's only source of income is her salary from a full-time job she has held for four years. She is paid $1,400 every two weeks. Her stable monthly income is ____________.

2. Match the following terms:

___ housing expense	a. PITI
___ income ratios	b. can be expected to continue
___ W2 forms	c. from a reliable source
___ income durability	d. measure adequacy of stable monthly income
___ income quality	e. verification of employment income

3. The two types of income ratios are the ____________________ to income ratio and the ____________________ to income ratio.

4. PITI stands for ________________, ________________, ________________, and ________________.

5. Indicate whether each of the following statements is true or false.

   A loan applicant's stable monthly income must qualify under both types of income ratios in order for the loan to be approved. T F

   When calculating income ratios, the lender takes into account the applicant's monthly expense for food and clothing. T F

   Stable monthly income is the applicant's take-home pay after deductions for income tax and social security. T F

Exercise 13E

1. To calculate an individual's net worth, subtract ______________________ from ______________________.

2. Cash and other assets that can easily be turned into cash are called ___________ ______________.

3. A borrower who does not have enough money for the downpayment and closing costs is allowed to use ____________ funds from a relative, but may not use ______________________ funds. The relative would be required to sign a ______________________.

4. Match the following terms:

___ reserves	a. real estate for sale
___ liabilities	b. jewelry, cars, real estate, furniture
___ assets	c. cash left over after closing
___ liquid assets	d. credit cards, charge accounts, other debts
___ net equity	e. money in the bank, stocks

5. The form used by lenders to verify an applicant's bank balance is called ________ ____.

Exercise 13F

1. List five types of negative information that can show up on a credit report.
   1. ____________________________________
   2. ____________________________________
   3. ____________________________________
   4. ____________________________________
   5. ____________________________________

2. Most negative items will remain on a person's credit report for _____ years. The items that will remain on a credit report for 10 years are __________________ __________________.

3. Indicate whether each of the following statements is true or false.

   Bill consolidation or refinancing is always considered a negative factor on a credit report. T F

   Credit reports typically include information regarding the applicant's payment history for utility and doctor bills. T F

   If an applicant meets the lender's standards for income and net worth, an unsatisfactory credit rating by itself will not be enough to disqualify the applicant for the loan. T F

4. Derogatory credit information is less likely to have a negative affect on a loan application if the applicant can show that:

   1. ______________________________ and
   2. ______________________________

Lesson 13: Workbook Quiz Questions

1. Jake joined a company when it first opened six months ago. This would cause an underwriter to be concerned about:
   a. the quality of Jake's income
   b. his company's retirement plan
   c. tax withholding
   d. his family's contribution

2. Income that will cease in the near future does not meet standards of:
   a. quantity
   b. durability
   c. dependability
   d. net worth

3. The general rule is that a loan applicant should have continuous employment in the same field for at least:
   a. six months
   b. one year
   c. two years
   d. three years

4. In evaluating a potential borrower for a loan, which of the following does an underwriter consider?
   a. Credit history
   b. Income
   c. Net worth
   d. All of the above

5. Income that meets underwriting standards of quality and durability is known as:
   a. financial worth
   b. net worth
   c. solid assets
   d. stable monthly income

6. Which of the following types of income does not qualify as stable monthly income?
   a. Regular unemployment compensation
   b. Regular annual bonuses
   c. Regular overtime pay
   d. Regular pay for commissions

7. A loan applicant is likely to be asked to provide audited financial statements and federal tax returns if his or her primary source of income is:
   a. self-employment
   b. social security payments
   c. public assistance
   d. unemployment compensation

8. Which of the following factors is most likely to disqualify child support payments from inclusion in stable monthly income?
   a. The payments are required by court order
   b. The child is 17 years old
   c. The payments have been made for five years
   d. The payor lives in another state

9. To allow for unpredictable factors related to this type of income, an underwriter might include only a percentage of it in stable monthly income:
   a. investment income
   b. alimony
   c. rental income
   d. public assistance

10. A co-mortgagor is one who:
    a. lives on the mortgaged property with the primary mortgagor
    b. rents the mortgaged property from the mortgagor
    c. takes equitable title to the property
    d. takes responsibility for repaying the mortgage loan

11. Which of the following will generally be considered in calculating stable monthly income?
    a. Self-employment income
    b. Income from a temporary job
    c. Unemployment compensation
    d. Income from a family member

12. Milton receives a paycheck every two weeks in the amount of $1,200. His stable monthly income is:
    a. $2,600
    b. $2,400
    c. $3,000
    d. $3,600

13. A percentage that is applied to assess the adequacy of a loan applicant's stable monthly income is called:
    a. a probability percentage
    b. an income ratio
    c. a cost/benefit ratio
    d. a projected potential earnings ratio

14. Janet and Ken Stillman have a stable monthly income of $8,000. The house they would like to buy would require a monthly mortgage payment of $2,000. Their only debts are a car payment of $300 a month and business loan of $100 a month. What would the housing expense to income ratio be for this loan?
    a. 40%
    b. 30%
    c. 25%
    d. 20%

15. The figure sometimes called "PITI" includes:
    a. the loan origination fee
    b. personal assets minus liabilities
    c. the debt to income ratio
    d. a portion of the property taxes

16. Cash and other assets, such as stocks, that can be easily converted to cash, are called:
    a. negotiable instruments
    b. liquid assets
    c. net worth
    d. net assets

17. A lender may require the borrower to have which of the following after paying the downpayment and closing costs?
    a. Credit report
    b. Financial analysis
    c. Debt consolidation
    d. Reserves

18. For an underwriter, which of the following would raise questions about the suitability of a loan applicant?
    a. A bank account balance that is significantly higher than the average balance
    b. A bank account opened one year ago
    c. The existence of an audited financial statement
    d. A debt to income ratio below 30%

19. For underwriting purposes, net equity in real estate for sale is:
    a. the difference between the property's market value and total liens against the property plus selling expenses
    b. the difference between market value and sales price
    c. not a liquid asset
    d. excluded from net worth

20. Andrew is applying for an institutional loan to buy a home. He doesn't have enough cash for the downpayment, but his aunt is willing to loan him the money he needs. From the institutional lender's point of view, the loan from the aunt:

    a. will be considered part of Andrew's net worth, as long as the repayment terms are in writing
    b. will be accepted, but only as a non-liquid asset
    c. is an acceptable source of funds if the loan is made long enough before closing
    d. will not be an acceptable arrangement

21. Abigail has applied for a loan to buy a new house. She also owns a ski cabin that she doesn't plan to sell. Abigail's equity in the cabin:

    a. is a liquid asset
    b. is a liability
    c. is a non-liquid asset
    d. is not part of her net worth

22. A gift letter:

    a. confirms that a gift is not a loan
    b. must be verified by the underwriter
    c. cannot represent funds borrowed by the donor
    d. All of the above

23. A personal credit report includes information from the past:

    a. three years
    b. five years
    c. seven years
    d. ten years

24. Which of the following would not normally appear in a credit report?

    a. Late payment of a dental bill
    b. Phone bill sent to a collection agency
    c. Bankruptcy
    d. Repossession of stereo bought on credit

25. Theresa's client wants to finance a home purchase, but anticipates an unfavorable credit report. Theresa should:

    a. tell the client to wait seven years to clear his record
    b. tell her client to get a lender's opinion of the likelihood of being able to obtain loan approval
    c. write a personal recommendation for her client to submit with his loan application
    d. offer to act as co-mortgagor for her client

Lesson 14

Real Estate Finance: Finance Programs

Exercise 14A

1. The uniform underwriting standards that lenders use for most conventional home loans are set by ____________________ and ____________________.

2. The Yamaguchis make a $988 mortgage payment each month. The lender applies part of the payment to interest and the rest to principal; each month, slightly less goes toward interest, and slightly more goes toward principal. This means that the Yamaguchis have a/an __________________ loan.

3. Indicate whether each of the following statements is true or false.

   At the end of the loan term, the balance of a fully amortized loan is equal to zero. T F

   With an amortized loan, the amount of the payment that is applied to interest increases each month. T F

   Almost all conventional loans are fully amortized. T F

4. The payment amount for a partially amortized loan is calculated on the basis of a repayment period that is (longer / shorter) than the actual term of the loan.

5. At the end of the loan term of a partially amortized loan, the borrower must make a lump sum payment of the remaining principal balance. This payment is called __________________________.

Exercise 14B

1. Match the following terms:

___ nonconforming loan	a. substantial interest savings
___ conventional loan	b. balloon payment required
___ fully amortized loan	c. standard residential loan term
___ partially amortized loan	d. won't be purchased by secondary market agencies
___ 30-year loan	e. not guaranteed by a government agency
___ 15-year loan	f. regular payments pay off loan by end of term

2. In contrast to a 30-year loan, a 15-year loan is likely to involve (circle all that are correct):
   a. a higher interest rate
   b. a higher monthly payment
   c. a lower downpayment
   d. less interest paid overall

3. A balloon payment is required in connection with (circle all that are correct):
   a. fully amortized loans
   b. partially amortized loans
   c. interest only loans

4. Why do lenders charge a lower interest rate for 15-year loans than for 30-year loans?

   ____

5. The majority of the savings from a 15-year loan is a result of:
   a. the lower interest rate
   b. the shorter repayment period

Exercise 14C

1. The Duponts have taken out a 30-year loan at 8.75% interest. The interest rate will not change during the loan term, so this is a/an ______________ loan.

2. Which of the following can increase or decrease during the term of an adjustable-rate mortgage? (Circle all that are correct.)
   a. Index rate
   b. Margin
   c. Interest rate charged to borrower
   d. Monthly payment amount
   e. Payment adjustment period

3. List two ARM features that help prevent payment shock.
   1. ______________________________
   2. ______________________________

4. Match the following terms:

___	margin	a.	unpaid interest added to principal
___	negative amortization	b.	switch to fixed rate
___	index	c.	one-year ARM
___	conversion option	d.	lender's profit
___	rate adjustment period	e.	published statistical report

5. Indicate whether each of the following statements is true or false.

   With an ARM, the borrower rather than the lender bears the risk of fluctuations in market interest rates. T F

   Regardless of changes in market interest rates, the index for an ARM always stays the same. T F

   For most ARMs, payment adjustments are made at the same time as rate adjustments. T F

6. What is a conversion option?

   ____

Exercise 14D

1. The loan-to-value ratio expresses the relationship between the ______________ and the ______________________ or the ______________________________ of the property, whichever is less.

2. Carl Grunbaum is buying a house for $102,000; the appraised value is $100,000. He is financing the purchase with an $87,000 loan. The loan-to- value ratio for this loan is _____ %. The lender will treat it as a _____ % loan.

3. Lenders generally require private mortgage insurance for (circle all that are correct):

   a. 80% loans

   b. 90% loans

   c. 95% loans

4. Lenders generally require owner-occupancy for (circle all that are correct):

   a. 80% loans

   b. 90% loans

   c. 95% loans

5. Private mortgage insurance protects the ____________ from losses resulting from ____________________________.

Exercise 14E

1. For a $150,000 loan, one point amounts to $__________.

2. List the two types of points that lenders charge:

   1. __________________________

   2. __________________________

3. A lender may charge ____________________ in order to increase the yield on the loan.

4. Buydowns are more common when market interest rates ____________________.

5. List the two ways in which a buydown helps the buyer:
   1. ____
   2. ____

Exercise 14F

1. In calculating a conventional loan applicant's total debt service ratio, the underwriter takes into account all recurring obligations with ____________ payments remaining.

2. Match the following:

___ 28%	a. maximum total debt service ratio applied by some lenders for 95% loans
___ 33%	b. maximum housing expense to income ratio
___ 36%	c. maximum total debt service ratio for most loans

3. The Swansons have a stable monthly income of $4,000. They are applying for a conventional loan that would have a monthly payment of $980. They won't qualify for the loan unless their recurring obligations (aside from the proposed mortgage payment) amount to no more than $ ________ per month.

4. A conventional borrower is generally required to have at least ____ months' mortgage payments in reserve after closing.

5. Lena Smith is buying a house for $100,000, and she's financing the purchase with a $90,000 loan. Smith's parents can help her out with gift funds, as long as Smith invests at least $ __________ of her own money in the transaction.

Exercise 14G

1. Unlike a conventional borrower, an FHA borrower is allowed to finance __________ __________________ along with the purchase price.

2. The loan term for an FHA loan is usually _____ years, but may be as short as _____ years.

3. The FHA's mortgage insurance plan is called ____________________________. Most FHA-insured loans are made under the standard ________ program. The two basic requirements to qualify for this program are:

   1. ____
   2. ____

4. List three advantages to an FHA loan in comparison to conventional loans.

   1. ____
   2. ____
   3. ____

5. Indicate whether each of the following statements is true or false.

   The one-time premium for FHA insurance can either be paid at closing or financed over the life of the loan. T F

   The annual premium for FHA insurance must be paid at closing. T F

   The term "MIP" refers to both the one-time premium and the annual premiums for FHA financing. T F

   FHA loans may be made for as much as 97% of the home's appraised value. T F

   The maximum amount for an FHA loan depends on the borrower's income. T F

Exercise 14H

1. Indicate whether each of the following statements is true or false?

   Only low-income buyers are eligible for FHA loans. T F

   Mortgage insurance is only required on FHA loans with LTVs over 95%. T F

   FHA loans typically require a smaller downpayment than conventional loans. T F

   An FHA loan cannot be assumed. T F

   There are maximum loan amounts for FHA loans, which depend on the cost of housing in the area in question. T F

2. When a borrower takes out a second loan in order to supplement the main loan, it's called ______________________________.

3. It is (easier / harder) to qualify for an FHA loan than a conventional loan. The maximum fixed payment to income ratio for an FHA loan is _______ %.

4. List the 5 conditions that must be met if secondary financing is to be used in conjunction with an FHA-insured primary loan.

   1. ______________________________
   2. ______________________________
   3. ______________________________
   4. ______________________________
   5. ______________________________

5. Following is a list of terms that are commonly used in reference to conventional loans. For each term, list the corresponding term that is used in reference to FHA loans.

   a. stable monthly income ______________________________

   b. housing expense to income ratio ______________________________

   c. total debt service ratio ______________________________

   d. PMI ______________________________

Exercise 14I

1. To obtain a VA-guaranteed loan, an eligible veteran should submit an application to (circle all that are correct):

   a. an institutional lender

   b. the Dept. of Housing and Urban Development

   c. the Veterans Administration

2. Indicate whether each of the following statements is true or false?

   A veteran buying property with a VA loan must intend to occupy the property. T F

   The maximum loan amount for a VA loan is $145,000. T F

   A VA loan can only be assumed by an eligible veteran. T F

   Mortgage insurance is not required for VA loans. T F

3. If a VA loan is assumed by the buyer when a property is sold, what conditions must be met in order for the seller to restore his full VA entitlement?

   1. ______________________________
   2. ______________________________
   3. ______________________________

4. What are the four conditions that must be satisfied in order for a buyer to use secondary financing in connection with a VA loan?

   1. ______________________________
   2. ______________________________
   3. ______________________________
   4. ______________________________

5. Although VA borrowers do not need to pay a mortgage insurance premium, the VA does charge a funding fee of up to ______________________________.

Exercise 14J

1. To obtain a VA loan, an eligible veteran must qualify under both the income ratio method and the ______________________ method.

2. Place the following phrases under the appropriate headings shown below.

   a. No downpayment required

   b. Financed closing costs

   c. Reserves required after closing

   d. 80%, 90%, 95%

   e. Residual income

   f. Mortgage insurance always required

CONVENTIONAL	FHA-INSURED	VA-GUARANTEED

3. The income ratio used in qualifying a borrower for VA financing is called ________ ______________________. In most cases, this ratio may not exceed _____ %.

4. List the three factors that determine the amount of residual income needed to qualify for a VA loan.

   1. ______________________
   2. ______________________
   3. ______________________

5. Indicate whether each of the following statements is true or false.

   The qualifying standards for VA loans are significantly more lenient than those for conventional loans. T F

   In most cases, the VA guaranty covers the full loan amount. T F

   If the lender charges discount points on a VA loan, the points may not be paid by the borrower. T F

   The interest rate for a VA loan is negotiable between the borrower and the lender. T F

Lesson 14: Workbook Quiz Questions

1. A loan that does not meet the standards set by Fannie Mae and Freddie Mac is called:
   a. a nonconforming loan
   b. an unconventional loan
   c. a disamortized loan
   d. a secondary market loan

2. A fully amortized loan:
   a. has interest-only payments
   b. is paid off by the end of the loan term with regular payments of principal and interest
   c. is paid off in half the time it takes to pay off a partially amortized loan
   d. cannot have a fixed interest rate

3. A balloon payment is a feature of:
   a. an adjustable-rate mortgage
   b. a 15-year loan
   c. a partially amortized loan
   d. a conforming loan

4. In comparison to a 30-year loan for the same amount, a 15-year loan:
   a. will require a higher monthly payment
   b. is likely to have a lower interest rate
   c. will save the borrower thousands of dollars in total interest charges over the life of the loan
   d. All of the above

5. In connection with an ARM, an index is:
   a. a limit on the amount the payment can increase per year
   b. 2% to 3% of the loan amount
   c. the interval at which the loan's interest rate is adjusted
   d. a published statistical report that indicates changes in the cost of money

6. For most ARMs, the monthly mortgage payment:
   a. is adjusted each time the interest rate is adjusted
   b. is adjusted more often than the interest rate
   c. is adjusted only once every five years
   d. is not increased or decreased during the loan term

7. If a loan's monthly payments do not cover all the interest owed, the lender may add the unpaid interest to the principal balance. This is called:
   a. negative amortization
   b. partial amortization
   c. a conversion option
   d. the lender's margin

8. The lower the loan-to-value ratio:
   a. the larger the loan amount and the smaller the downpayment
   b. the smaller the loan amount and the larger the downpayment
   c. the smaller the loan amount and the smaller the downpayment
   d. None of the above

9. Lenders use loan-to-value ratios:
   a. to increase the yield on their loans
   b. to reduce the interest rate charged to the borrower
   c. to set maximum loan amounts
   d. to amortize their loans

10. A loan's LTV expresses the relationship between the loan amount and:
    a. the sales price
    b. the appraised value
    c. the sales price or the appraised value, whichever is more
    d. the sales price or the appraised value, whichever is less

11. Private mortgage insurance is generally required:
    a. for 90% and 95% conventional loans
    b. only for 95% conventional loans
    c. for 80%, 90%, and 95% conventional loans
    d. for all conventional loans

12. In real estate finance, one point is one percent of:
    a. the loan amount
    b. the sales price
    c. the appraised value
    d. the sales price or the appraised value, whichever is less

13. Points paid at closing to increase the lender's yield on the loan are called:
    a. the origination fee
    b. discount points
    c. index points
    d. the margin

14. A loan origination fee:
    a. is refunded to the borrower at closing
    b. must not exceed 1% of the loan amount
    c. is charged in virtually every residential loan transaction
    d. All of the above

15. A buydown:
    a. can be permanent or temporary
    b. lowers the buyer's monthly payment
    c. makes it easier to qualify for the loan
    d. All of the above

16. For most conventional loans, the borrower's total debt service ratio should not exceed:
    a. 25%
    b. 36%
    c. 41%
    d. 50%

17. A conventional borrower:
    a. must have a residual income of at least $1,800
    b. must have a stable monthly income of at least $3,000
    c. is not allowed to use any gift funds for the downpayment
    d. is required to have at least two months' mortgage payments in reserve after closing

18. The primary function of the Federal Housing Administration is:
    a. insuring mortgage loans
    b. funding mortgage loans
    c. arranging mortgage loans
    d. building affordable housing

19. The downpayment (minimum cash investment) required in connection with an FHA loan:
    a. is often less than the downpayment required for a comparable conventional loan
    b. is often less than the downpayment required for a comparable VA loan
    c. must be at least 20% of the property's appraised value
    d. must be at least 25% of the property's appraised value

20. One of the advantages of an FHA loan is that:
    a. mortgage insurance is not required
    b. the borrower is not required to occupy the home purchased with the loan
    c. the interest rate cannot exceed 8%
    d. the borrower is allowed to finance the closing costs

21. Which of the following statements about qualifying for an FHA loan is true?
    a. A residual income test is used instead of income ratios
    b. The borrower must meet residual income requirements as well as the income ratio tests
    c. The FHA qualifying standards are less stringent than conventional standards
    d. Home buyers with an annual household gross income over $35,000 are not eligible for an FHA loan

22. The property purchased with a VA loan:
    a. must be a single-family home that the veteran intends to occupy
    b. can be any single-family home, whether or not the veteran intends to occupy it
    c. can be any real estate that meets federal collateral standards
    d. can be any one- to four-unit residence, as long as the veteran intends to occupy one of the units

23. One distinguishing characteristic of VA loans is that:
    a. the loan amount cannot exceed $46,000
    b. they cannot be assumed
    c. no downpayment is required
    d. the borrower does not have to pay interest

24. In evaluating whether an eligible veteran qualifies for a VA loan, an underwriter must consider:
    a. residual income requirements
    b. maximum income limits
    c. the housing expense to income ratio
    d. the appraised value to income ratio

25. The VA guaranty:
    a. ensures that every veteran can obtain a loan
    b. reduces the lender's risk of loss in case of default
    c. protects the veteran borrower from default
    d. All of the above

Lesson 15

Real Estate Appraisal

Exercise 15A

1. It is a violation of an appraiser's fiduciary duty to reveal his or her estimate of the property's value without the client's consent.

2. True or false? Washington law requires all appraisers working in the state to be certified. T (F)

3. What is the definition of appraisal? an estimate or opinion of value

4. List five situations that commonly require a real estate appraisal.
   1. setting a sales price
   2. " a loan amt
   3. estate liquidations
   4. property management
   5. property tax assessments

5. Most appraisers follow the guidelines established by the Appraisal Foundation. These guidelines are known as Uniform standards of Professional Appraisal Practice.

Exercise 15B

1. Match the equivalent terms (more than one can apply):

b, d	utility value	a.	value in exchange
a	market value	b.	value in use
c	market price	c.	sales price
		d.	subjective value

2. A sale under ideal conditions is also known as a/an arms length transaction transaction.

3. The type of value that is estimated in most appraisals is market value.

4. The most widely accepted definition of market value is found in uniform standards of prof. appraisal.

5. Indicate whether each of the following statements is true or false.

   Value in use is a more objective standard than value in exchange. T F

   Market price is more likely to represent market value if the sale was an arm's length transaction. T F

   Two separate appraisals should always come up with the same market value, assuming the appraisers are competent. T F

Exercise 15C

1. An appraisal is always made as of a specific point in time, because of the principle of change

2. A property's highest and best use is the use that would bring the owner the greatest net.

3. List the three major forces that interact to create, support or erode property values.
   1. social ideas & standards
   2. economic fluctuations
   3. gov't regulations
4. List the four stages in the real estate cycle.
   1. integration (or development)
   2. equilibrium - when property is relatively stable
   3. disintegration
   4. rejuvenation
5. Indicate whether each of the following statements is true or false.

   When determining a property's highest and best use, an appraiser must take into account any public or private restrictions that apply to the property. (T) F

   A property's economic life is usually longer than its physical life. T (F)

   An increase in supply tends to cause values to increase. T (F)

Exercise 15D

1. Match each principle of value to the appropriate description:

e highest and best use	a. buyers won't pay more for one property than they would have to pay for an equivalent property
h change	b. related principles are those of regression and progression
f supply and demand	c. relates to the addition to value
a substitution	d. especially relevant in appraising income property
b conformity	e. refers to most profitable use
c contribution	f. an aspect of general economic theory
g anticipation	g. buyers' expectations are considered
d competition	h. related to life cycle

2. The tendency of a property's value to increase as a result of its location among more desirable properties is known as progression. The corresponding effect on the surrounding properties is called regression.

3. In appraising an improved property, an appraiser is more likely to be concerned with:
   a. the cost of the improvements
   b. the contribution of the improvements to value

4. Indicate whether each of the following statements is true or false.

   According to the principle of conformity, values are maximized when all the homes in a neighborhood have the same floor plan. T F

   The past history of the market is more relevant to an appraiser than the potential future of the market. T F

   An appraisal is always made of a specific date, called the effective date of the appraisal. T F

Exercise 15E

1. Place each of the following under the heading below that describes the context in which it would be evaluated during an appraisal:
   a. energy efficiency of building
   b. corner location
   c. amount of water frontage
   d. condition of streets
   e. proximity to schools
   f. topography of lot
   g. applicable zoning ordinances

NEIGHBORHOOD ANALYSIS	SITE ANALYSIS	BUILDING ANALYSIS
d, e, g	b, c, f	a

2. The results from each valuation method are called value indicators.

3. List the seven basic steps in the appraisal process.
   1. define problem
   2. determine what data is needed
   3. gather & verify general data
   4. " " " specific data
   5. select & apply valuation methods
   6. reconcile value indicators for final est. of value
   7. issue appraisal report

4. In order to define an appraisal problem, an appraiser must (circle all that apply):
   a. identify the subject property
   b. identify the approach to value
   c. establish the function of the appraisal
   d. determine how the client intends to use the appraisal
   e. establish the appraisal fee

5. Information concerning matters outside the subject property is called general data, while information about the subject property itself is known as specific data.

Exercise 15F

1. To be an accurate indication of value, the date of a comparable sale generally should be within the past 6 mo. (insert a time period).

2. The element of comparison that ordinarily has the greatest impact on value is location.

3. List the three approaches to value used by appraisers.
   1. sales comparison
   2. cost approach
   3. income approach

4. Why is the date of a comparable sale an important element of comparison?
 Values constantly change so past sales don't represent present property values

5. When making adjustments to account for differences in physical characteristics, the appraiser adjusts:
   a. the sales prices of the comparables
   b. the sales price of the subject property

Exercise 15G

1. True or false? An appraiser is bound to give equal weight to each comparable sale to arrive at a value for the property under consideration. T F

2. What is the minimum number of comparable sales that an appraiser will consider in the sales comparison approach? 3

3. List the primary elements of comparison for the sales comparison approach.
   1. date of sale
   2. location
   3. physical characteristics
   4. terms of sale

4. If a comparable sale was not an arm's length transactions, the appraiser will most likely not use it as comparison

---

Exercise 15H

1. Match the term with the correct definition:

a replacement cost	a.	the cost of improvements with the same utility as those being appraised
b reproduction cost	b.	the cost of constructing a building identical to the one being appraised

2. In the cost approach, the appraiser determines the replacement cost of the improvements.

3. Three different methods for estimating replacement cost are:
   1. the square foot method
   2. the unit -in-place method
   3. the quantity survey method

4. List the three types of depreciation:
   1. deferred maintanence
   2. functional obsolescence
   3. external "

5. Which one of the three types of depreciation in the preceding answer is virtually always incurable? external obsolescence

6. From the estimated replacement cost, the appraiser subtracts the total amount of depreciation.

7. In the cost approach, the appraiser arrives at estimated land value by using the sales comparison approach.

Exercise 15I

1. Match each term with the correct description or definition:

c economic rent	a. the potential gross income minus the bad debt/vacancy factor
d contract rent	b. effective gross income minus total operating expenses
a effective gross income	c. potential gross income
b net income	d. current actual rent

2. Which item does not belong in the following list?
   a. utility expenses
   b. property taxes
   c. monthly mortgage payments
   d. repairs

3. What makes the item selected in the previous question different from the others? mortgage pyt's aren't considered as operating costs

4. What is the capitalization formula? annual net income ÷ capitalization rate = value

5. If a property's net income is $11,400 and the capitalization rate is 12%, what is the value of the property? 95,000

6. The higher an investment's risk, the (higher / lower) its capitalization rate.

Exercise 15J

1. True or false? The gross rent multiplier method is merely a simpler version of the income approach to value. T F

2. In order to determine the gross rent multiplier of a subject property, divide the property's sales price by its monthly rent.

3. An appraiser must reconcile value indicators from the three approaches to reach a final estimate of market value.

4. The form used by most lenders for residential appraisals is the uniform residential appraisal Report.

Lesson 15: Workbook Quiz Questions

1. An appraisal:
   a. is an estimate or opinion of value
   b. is required by law before property can be transferred
   c. must be performed by a state-certified appraiser
   d. All of the above

2. The purpose of most appraisals is:
   a. determining the property's value in use
   b. estimating the property's market value
   c. certifying the property's utility value
   d. confirming the property's market price

3. "The most probable price which a property should bring in a competitive and open market under all conditions requisite to a fair sale" is a widely accepted definition of:
   a. highest and best use
   b. market price
   c. market value
   d. utility value

4. A sale will not be considered an arm's length transaction unless:
   a. the property was appraised before the purchase and sale agreement was signed
   b. the buyer intends to put the property to its highest and best use
   c. the price was adjusted to take into account accrued depreciation
   d. the buyer and seller were well informed and not acting under any unusual pressure

5. Highest and best use refers to the use that would:
   a. have the longest economic life
   b. generate the greatest historical and contract rent
   c. maximize the integration phase
   d. provide the greatest net return

6. The principle of substitution holds that:
   a. no one will pay more for a property than they would have to pay for an equally desirable substitute
   b. the value of a comparable property can be substituted for the value of the subject property
   c. during the equilibrium phase of a property's life cycle, value in use can be substituted for value in exchange
   d. for residential property, the gross multiplier method can be used in place of the income approach

7. The principle of anticipation holds that:
   a. value is created by the anticipated future benefits of owning a property
   b. a property's physical life invariably ends before its economic life
   c. values tend to rise as demand increases
   d. property values are generally expected to decline over the long run

8. An appraiser refers to information concerning matters outside the subject property that affect its value as:
   a. comparable data
   b. general data
   c. specific data
   d. site data

9. In a residential neighborhood, strictly enforced zoning and private restrictions:
   a. tend to depress property values
   b. have a regressive effect on the subject property
   c. promote conformity and protect property values
   d. prevent the highest and best use of the property

10. The sales comparison approach to value is also known as:
    a. the square foot method
    b. the capitalization approach
    c. the gross multiplier method
    d. the market data approach

11. In selecting comparables for the sales comparison approach, an appraiser looks for properties that:
    a. are similar to the subject property and have recently been sold
    b. cost the same amount to build as the subject property
    c. had similar assessed values in the most recent tax year
    d. are similar to the subject property and have generated the same historical rent

12. To appraise a single-family home using the sales comparison approach, an appraiser generally needs:
    a. at least three good comparables
    b. a recent quantity survey
    c. an accurate capitalization rate
    d. an estimate of accrued depreciation

13. The primary elements of comparison for the sales comparison approach include:
    a. terms of sale, contract rent, and replacement cost
    b. date of sale, location, and physical characteristics
    c. economic life, location, and depreciation
    d. physical characteristics, reserves for replacement, and listing price

14. In selecting comparables for the sales comparison approach, an appraiser must investigate the circumstances of each sale to determine whether:
    a. the investor realized the return that he or she expected
    b. the reproduction cost was the same as the replacement cost
    c. it was an arm's length transaction
    d. there was a bad debt/vacancy factor

15. In the sales comparison approach, after making all necessary adjustments to the prices of the comparables, the appraiser uses them to estimate the value of the subject property. The value estimate:
    a. is usually the highest of the adjusted prices
    b. should not be any greater than the lowest of the adjusted prices
    c. should be the median adjusted price
    d. is never merely an average of the adjusted prices

16. In the cost approach, the appraiser:
    a. subtracts the value of the land from the value of the improvements to estimate the accrued depreciation
    b. estimates the value of the improvements separately from the value of the land
    c. must estimate both the replacement cost of the improvements and the reproduction cost of the land
    d. capitalizes the value of the land and adds it to the reproduction cost of the improvements

16-B

17. Replacement cost (as opposed to reproduction cost) is:
    a. the original cost of constructing an exact duplicate of the subject building
    b. the original cost of constructing a building with the same utility as the subject building
    c. the current cost of constructing an exact duplicate of the subject building
    d. the current cost of constructing a building with the same utility as the subject building

18. The simplest way to estimate replacement cost is:
    a. the square foot method
    b. the unit-in-place method
    c. the quantity survey method
    d. the benchmark method

19. Depreciation is classified as:
    a. deferred maintenance, functional obsolescence, or external obsolescence
    b. deferred maintenance, incurable obsolescence, or external obsolescence
    c. curable obsolescence, functional obsolescence, or debt service
    d. deferred maintenance, curable obsolescence, or plottage

20. Which of the following is an example of functional obsolescence?
    a. A loss in value because of a high crime rate in the neighborhood
    b. A loss in value because of a leaking roof
    c. A loss in value because of noise from a nearby airport
    d. A loss in value because of outdated bathroom and kitchen fixtures

21. Which of the following is an example of external obsolescence?
    a. A loss in value because of cracks in the building's foundation
    b. A loss in value because of an extremely small kitchen
    c. A loss in value because of odors from a nearby factory
    d. A loss in value because of a poor floor plan

22. The rent that a property would generate if it were currently available for lease on the open market is called the:
    a. contract rent
    b. historical rent
    c. gross rent
    d. economic rent

23. A bad debt/vacancy factor is:
    a. only used in the gross rent multiplier method
    b. a percentage of the property's operating expenses
    c. deducted from potential gross income to arrive at effective gross income
    d. deducted from the property's debt service to arrive at the capitalization rate

24. In the income approach to value, an appraiser deducts the property's operating expenses from its effective gross income to arrive at its:
    a. net income
    b. capitalization income
    c. reserves for replacement
    d. adjusted gross income

25. The capitalization rate used in the income approach is:
    a. the rate of depreciation that is affecting the subject property's value
    b. the rate of return an investor would be likely to demand from the subject property
    c. the rate at which the subject property's value has increased over the past ten years
    d. the rate at which the subject property's value is expected to increase over the next five years

net income ÷ capitalization rate = value

Escrow and Settlement Statements

Exercise 16A

1. Once a buyer or seller has placed an item (a document, a sum of money, etc.) in escrow, the escrow agent cannot return it to that party except:
   1. in accordance with a provision in the ~~escrow agreement~~ instructions, or
   2. if the other party agrees.
2. A real estate broker is allowed to provide escrow services (without complying with the Escrow Agent Registration Act) in transactions in which the broker is already representing one of the parties, as long as the broker does not charge a commission for those services.
3. In a typical real estate transaction, which party does the escrow agent represent, the buyer or the seller? both - dual agent
4. A company that is licensed to engage in the escrow business under the Escrow Agent Registration Act is called certified escrow agent.
5. Indicate whether each of the following statements is true or false.

   Escrow officers must take an exam and be properly licensed. (T) F

   When an escrow agent handles funds on behalf of buyers or sellers, the funds must be placed in a trust account maintained in a recognized Washington depository. (T) F

   Institutional lenders are generally exempt from the Escrow Agent Registration Act. (T) F

Exercise 16B

1. On a simplified settlement statement, there are four columns: buyer's debits, buyer's credits, seller's debits, and seller's credits. The total at the bottom of the buyer's debits column is supposed to equal the total at the bottom of the Credit column. And the total at the bottom of the seller's debits column is supposed to equal the total at the bottom of the Credit column.

2. When a settlement item is payable by the buyer to the seller, how is it shown on the settlement statement?

   buyers debit ; sellers Credit

3. When allocating closing costs, the escrow agent is guided by:

   1. escrow instructions
   2. purchase & sale agreement
   3. local customs

4. When a closing cost is payable BY a party, it shows up as a debit on the party's settlement statement; costs that are payable TO a party are listed as credit on the party's statement.

5. Indicate whether each of the following statements is true or false.

   All the information that an escrow agent needs in order to prepare a settlement statement can be found in the purchase and sale agreement. T (F)

   In most closings of residential transactions, the escrow agent uses a Uniform Settlement Statement. (T) F

   A settlement statement is nothing more than a brief statement presenting all of the financial details of the closing. (T) F

Exercise 16C

1. When a seller has an existing mortgage that will be paid off at closing, the escrow agent will need to know the amounts for payoff amt + any pre-payment penalty, and reserve acct bal.. These agent will obtain these amounts from the lender.

2. Appraisal, credit report and survey fees are normally charged to the buyer at closing.

3. A buyer made an offer of $145,000, accompanied by a $5,000 earnest money deposit. The offer specified that the buyer would assume the seller's existing $70,000 mortgage balance. If the seller accepts the offer, what amount will be listed for the purchase price:

   on the seller's settlement statement? 145,000

   on the buyer's settlement statement? 145,000

4. The amount of any seller financing always appears on a settlement statement as debit to seller, credit to buyer

5. How would the broker's commission normally be shown on a settlement statement?

   as debit to seller

Exercise 16D

1. List the following items under the appropriate heading shown below, according to how each item is treated in a typical real estate transaction. Certain items may belong under two different headings.
   a. purchase price
   b. earnest money deposit
   c. broker's commission
   d. buyer's new loan from institutional lender
   e. excise tax
   f. seller financing

BUYER'S DEBITS	BUYER'S CREDITS	SELLER'S DEBITS	SELLER'S CREDITS
a	b, d, f	c, e, f	a

2. List three documents that are commonly recorded in connection with a sale of real estate, and the party responsible for paying the recording fee for each document.
   1. deed from seller to buyer (pd by buyer)
   2. buyer's mortgage or deed of trust (buyer)
   3. deed of reconveyance for sellers existing mortgage (seller)

3. Who customarily pays the insurance premium for:

   owner's title insurance seller

   lender's title insurance buyer

4. If personal property items are included in the sale, the escrow agent should request that the seller sign a bill of sale.

5. Who usually pays the escrow agent's fee? fee is split 50/50

Exercise 16E

1. In regard to prorated expenses, the buyer is usually responsible for paying the expense beginning with:

   a. the day before closing

   b. the day of closing

   c. the day after closing

2. List the three basic steps for prorating an expense.

   1. daily rate of expense (per diem rate)
   2. determine # of days each party is responsible
   3. multiply that # of days by per diem to determine that party's share

3. True or false? It is customary for escrow agents to prorate expenses on the basis of a standard 30-day month or 360-day year, in order to simplify the calculations.

   T F

4. How many days are there in each month?

   Jan 31 Feb 28 Mar 31 Apr 30 May 31 Jun 30

   Jul 31 Aug 31 Sep 30 Oct 31 Nov 30 Dec 31

5. In order for a proration to be accurate, the per diem rate for an annual expense should be calculated to an accuracy of at least 5 decimal places.

Exercise 16F

1. Brandon is buying Sorrento's house, and the closing date is February 20. This year's general real estate taxes are $1,168; Sorrento hasn't paid them yet. The escrow agent will prorate the taxes and list $ 160.00 as a debit for the seller on the settlement statement. (Use a 365-day year for the proration.)

2. A sale closes on November 2. If the annual property taxes of $2,125 have already been paid, how will they be shown on the settlement statement? (Use a 365-day year for the proration.)

   per diem 5.82192

   number of days 60

   prorated amount 349.32

   allocation on settlement statement 349.32

3. Hazard insurance premiums are typically paid:

   a. in advance

   b. in arrears

4. A sale closes on May 30. If the annual hazard insurance premium of $275 has been paid through April of the following year, what is the amount of the refund the seller is entitled to? (Use a 365-day year for the proration.)

   per diem 0675342

   number of days 336

   refund to seller 253.15

Exercise 16G

1. The closing date is August 16. The seller made the August 1 payment on his mortgage, but he will be required to pay interest on the loan at closing to cover the period from ____________ through ____________. The buyer won't be required to make a payment on her new mortgage until the first of ____________, but she will have to pay prepaid interest at closing to cover the period from ____________ through ____________.

2. A sale closes on March 10. The seller has made the March payment for her mortgage, which now has a balance of $83,402.88. Interest on the loan is 8.5% per year. How much interest will the seller owe at closing? (Use a 365-day year for the proration.)

   per diem ________

   number of days _____

   interest owed by seller ________

3. Interest on a mortgage loan is typically paid:
   a. in advance
   b. in arrears

4. A sale closes on July 4. The buyer has financed the purchase with a $165,000 loan at 9% interest. How much interest does the buyer owe at closing? (Use a 365-day year for the proration.)

   per diem __________

   number of days _____

   interest owed by buyer __________

5. A sale closes on July 4. Assuming that the buyer's loan payments are due on the first of each month, when will the buyer's first regular loan payment be due?

   ____

Exercise 16H

1. If the total of the buyer's debits is $189,438.55, and the total of the buyer's credits is $177,935.00, how much cash does the buyer need for closing?

   ____

2. If the total of the seller's debits is $131,446.73, and the total of the seller's credits is $181,314.47, how much will the seller receive at closing?

   ____

3. What happens if the total of the sellers debits exceeds the total of the seller's credits?

   seller needs to pay diff. in cash to close the sale

4. If the seller is paying off an existing loan against the property, what five items must the escrow agent consider in preparing this aspect of the seller's settlement statement?
   1. loan balance
   2. any unpd. interest
   3. any prepayment penalties
   4. any balance in sellers reserve acct.
   5. recording fee for satisfaction of mortgage
5. List three items that would normally show up on the settlement statement for both the buyer and the seller.
   1. purchase price
   2. property taxes
   3. seller financing

   recording fees, attorney fees, escrow fees etc..

Exercise 16I

1. Which of the following loan transactions would be covered by RESPA? (Circle all that are correct.) Assume that these are institutional loans secured by a first mortgage against the property purchased.
   a. A loan for the purchase of a six-unit apartment house
   b. A loan for the purchase of a single-family home
   c. A loan for the purchase of a lot with a mobile home
   d. A loan for the purchase of a lot zoned for commercial use
2. In loan transactions covered by RESPA, the borrower should receive a (circle all that are correct):
   a. HUD booklet concerning closing costs
   b. good faith estimate of closing costs
   c. Uniform Settlement Statement
   d. kickback

3. An escrow agent is required to report every sale of real property to the IRS. The agent must fill out Form 1099 with the seller's name and soc. sec. #, and the amount of the gross sale. If neither the escrow agent nor the mortgage lender files this form, it becomes the responsibility of the broker to do so.

4. RESPA requires the closing agent to allow the borrower to inspect the Uniform Settlement Statement within 1 before closing, if the borrower asks to do so.

5. If sale proceeds are not withheld from a seller who is subject to FIRPTA withholding, who is liable?

   anyone connected with sale

6. Indicate whether each of the following statements is true or false.

   RESPA never applies to a loan used to purchase vacant land. T F

   RESPA does not apply to a loan that is not a "federally related transaction". T F

   RESPA applies only to first mortgages or first deeds of trust. T F

figure out 3, 5, 9, 11, 12

Lesson 16: Workbook Quiz Questions

1. To help finance the purchase, the buyer is going to obtain a new 80% conventional loan. Where is the buyer's loan reflected in the settlement statement?
   a. Only as a debit for the buyer
   b. Only as a credit for the buyer
   c. As a credit for the buyer and a debit for the seller
   d. As a debit for the buyer and a credit for the seller

2. Where is prepaid interest noted on the settlement statement?
   a. Only as a credit for the seller
   b. Only as a credit for the buyer
   c. Only as a debit for the seller
   d. Only as a debit for the buyer

3. The seller's annual hazard insurance policy is paid through December 31, in the amount of $296. The transaction closes on October 20. The seller is not responsible for the day of closing. If prorations are calculated on a 360-day basis, the hazard insurance will appear on the settlement statement as a:
   a. $58.38 credit to the seller
   b. $58.38 debit to the seller
   c. $237.62 credit to the seller
   d. $237.62 debit to the seller

4. Which of the following would not be prorated at closing on the sale of a rental property?
   a. Prepaid property taxes
   b. Interest on seller's existing loan
   c. Security deposit
   d. Interest on buyer's new loan

5. A rental property is sold. The tenant paid the $900 monthly rent on the first of the month, and the transaction closed on the tenth of the month. Which of the following statements is true?
   a. Seller owes buyer $600
   b. Buyer owes seller $600
   c. Seller owes buyer $300
   d. Buyer owes seller $300

6. The buyer's earnest money deposit appears on the settlement statement as a:
   a. debit for the buyer, and as a credit for the seller
   b. credit for the buyer, and as a debit for the seller
   c. credit for the buyer only
   d. debit for the buyer only

7. If an earnest money deposit is in the form of a promissory note, it is noted on the settlement statement as a:
   a. debit for the buyer
   b. credit for the buyer
   c. credit for the seller
   d. None of the above; it is not listed

8. What is the primary purpose of the settlement statement?
   a. To account for, in detail, each party's expenses and credits, and the amount each will receive or be required to pay at closing
   b. To disclose the true costs of financing to both buyer and seller
   c. To provide documentary evidence of closing costs for state and federal authorities
   d. To provide the necessary documentation for a proper conveyance of title

9. The property appraisal cost $250. In a typical real estate transaction, the expense would be listed as a:
   a. $125 debit to the buyer and $125 debit to the seller
   b. $250 debit to the buyer
   c. $250 debit to the seller
   d. $250 debit to the buyer and a $250 credit to the seller

10. Which of the following would normally be a debit to the buyer?
   a. Commission
   b. Unpaid property taxes
   c. Standard policy of title insurance
   d. Loan origination fee

11. If the annual property taxes are $2,156, what would the per diem rate be for proration purposes if the calculations are based on a 360-day year?
   a. $5.91
   b. $5.99
   c. $6.01
   d. $6.10

12. On April 11, the buyer obtained a new loan in the amount of $134,000 at 8.25% annual interest. The first payment was due on June 1. If the buyer is responsible for interest payments starting on April 11, how much prepaid interest will the buyer be required to pay at closing? (Base your calculations on 360-day year.)
   a. $575.47
   b. $605.75
   c. $614.17
   d. $619.68

13. RESPA applies to all of the following except:
   a. a purchase money first loan made by a bank
   b. a senior mortgage loan made by a mortgage banker to finance a condominium unit
   c. a loan used to finance 50 acres for residential development
   d. a VA loan used to finance a fourplex

14. Under the Real Estate Settlement Procedures Act, a lender must provide the borrower with:
   a. a Uniform Settlement Statement
   b. a property disclosure statement
   c. the loan's annual percentage rate
   d. certified copies of buyer and seller closing statements

15. Which of the following is true about a settlement statement?
   a. The sum of one party's debits must equal the sum of the other party's credits
   b. The buyer's total debits and credits must match the seller's total debits and credits
   c. The buyer's total debits must equal the buyer's total credits
   d. The balance due to the seller is listed in the seller's credit column

16. A property is sold on a land contract. Where in the settlement statement would the contract price be noted?
   a. Only as debit for the buyer
   b. Only as a debit for the seller
   c. As a credit for the buyer and a debit for the seller
   d. As a debit for the buyer and a credit for the seller

17. For an additional $200, the seller has agreed to include her refrigerator as a part of the real property transaction. In addition to the deed, the seller should sign:

    a. a bill of sale
    b. a uniform settlement statement
    c. an appraisal
    d. a voucher

18. When the buyer is assuming the seller's existing loan, where would the loan balance be listed in the settlement statement?

    a. As a credit for the buyer only
    b. As a debit for the buyer only
    c. As a credit for the buyer, and as a debit for the seller
    d. As a debit for the buyer, and as a credit for the seller

19. A refund for prepaid fire insurance would be listed on the settlement statement as a:

    a. debit to the buyer
    b. debit to the seller
    c. credit to the buyer
    d. credit to the seller

20. A company that is licensed to engage in the escrow business under the Escrow Agent Registration Act is called:

    a. a certified escrow agent
    b. a uniform settlement agent
    c. a settlement trustee
    d. an executor

21. All of the following are exempt from the Washington Escrow Agent Registration Act except:

    a. a title company
    b. an escrow company
    c. a savings and loan
    d. an attorney

22. Which of the following is designed to determine under what conditions and at what time the escrow agent will distribute the money and documents involved in a real estate transaction to the proper parties?

    a. Escrow instructions
    b. Uniform Settlement Statement
    c. Purchase and sale agreement
    d. Listing agreement

23. Which of the following functions would not be performed by the escrow agent?

    a. Preparing the deed
    b. Recording documents
    c. Giving legal advice
    d. Disbursing funds

24. Which of the following has the power to investigate the actions of any certified escrow agent?

    a. The Director of the Department of Licensing
    b. The Insurance Commissioner
    c. The Governor
    d. The Securities Commissioner

25. Another name for prepaid interest is:

    a. compound interest
    b. simple interest
    c. interim interest
    d. variable interest

Property Management

Exercise 17A

1. Most managed real estate is income-producing property. The income of the property determines its value. The source of a property's income is tenants.

2. List five factors that influence the state of the real estate market for income-producing properties.
   1. value & supply of $
   2. trends in occupancy rates
   3. market rentals
   4. general employment levels
   5. family size & lifestyle

3. What is the difference between a technical oversupply of property and an economic oversupply of property?

   technical oversupply - more units than tenants; economic oversupply - enough tenants but not enough money to pay rent

4. Describe the relationship between occupancy levels and property values.

   less space to rent - higher rents & less amenities property value goes ↑

5. Indicate whether each of the following statements is true or false.

Family size and life style have a significant impact on the value of residential income property. (T) F

When evaluating local employment levels, a property manager is concerned with the attitudes of consumers with regard to saving. (T) F

In times of increasing occupancy levels, property managers tend to reduce the level of services they offer to tenants. (T) F

Occupancy rates are affected by the law of supply and demand. (T) F

Exercise 17B

1. List the four basic types of income-producing properties.
   1. residential property
   2. office bldgs
   3. retail property
   4. industrial property

2. The type of property that usually has the highest rate of turnover among tenants is residential. The lowest rate of turnover is usually found in industrial property.

3. Rent for office property is customarily calculated on the basis of price per square foot.

4. Why is tenant selection so important in the context of retail property management?

   price of rent based on business's income; more business & revenue = stronger rent

5. Indicate whether each of the following statements is true or false.

   Property managers tend to specialize in one or two types of property. (T) F

   Residential property is likely to require a greater degree of maintenance than office property. T (F)

   Residential leases normally include an escalation clause to compensate for the high turnover rate. T (F)

Exercise 17C

1. Indicate whether each of the following statements is true or false.

   A property management agreement must be in writing and signed by both the property manager and the owner. (T) F

   The property management agreement creates an agency relationship between the property manager and the owner. (T) F

   It is important that the property management agreement not be too specific about the manager's scope of authority, in order to allow for flexibility in management decision making. T (F)

2. Which of the following points should be included in a property management agreement? (Circle all that apply.)

   (a.) The extent of the manager's authority
   (b.) A description of the property to be managed
   (c.) Provisions for reporting to the owner
   (d.) The type of property to be managed
   (e.) The form of the manager's compensation
   (f.) The expenses that the manager is expected to pay

3. What considerations should the management agreement address in regard to reporting by the property manager to the owner?

   how often mgr will report & how detailed reports should be

4. What is the difference between a management agreement and a management plan?

   management agreement is the contract; plan is the strategy for managing property

5. In preparing a management plan, the property manager must focus on owners goals for the property.

Exercise 17D

1. List the four basic steps in a property manager's preliminary analysis of a property.
   1. regional analysis
   2. neighborhood "
   3. property analysis
   4. market "

2. Where can a property manager find the data needed for a regional analysis?

   gov't & trade groups publications

3. Indicate whether each of the following statements is true or false.

   The purpose of neighborhood analysis is to evaluate the effects of the property's location. (T) F

   It is important for a property manager to understand the reasons behind any trends in neighborhood characteristics. (T) F

   A property's profitability is always affected by its location, regardless of the quality of property management. (T) F

4. Which of the following characteristics would a property manager evaluate in a property analysis?
   - (a.) Current occupancy rate and tenant composition
   - b. Economic status of neighborhood residents
   - c. Trends in population growth
   - (d.) Number and size of living units
   - (e.) Adequacy of parking spaces

Exercise 17E

1. What is the first step in a market analysis?

   defining the market for property

2. What is the purpose of performing a market analysis?

   see how property compares to competing properties + identify occ. levels + rent rates

3. List four factors that a property manager should consider in a market analysis.

   1. # of available units in area
   2. current rental rates
   3. current occ. levels for comparable units
   4. quality of average unit

4. Indicate whether each of the following statements is true or false.

   The owner's investment goals are a primary consideration in developing a management plan. T F

   A preliminary study of the property is usually performed only for non-residential income-producing properties. T F

   In performing a market analysis for a retail shopping center, a property manager will usually analyze all retail properties in the market area, regardless of size or configuration. T F

Exercise 17F

1. A list of all the rental rates assigned to the various units in a property is called a rental schedule

2. The two general categories of expenses that are included in a property management budget are fixed and variable.

3. What is the difference between a management plan and a management proposal?

   plan is mgr's strategy to implement goals; proposal is draft of plan + becomes plan when owner agrees

4. Indicate whether each of the following statements is true or false.

   Variable expenses include property taxes, insurance premiums, and staff salaries. T (F)

   A high vacancy rate may be an indication that rents are too high. (T) F

   A property's net operating income is equal to its total income minus its total expenses, including reserves for replacement. T (F)

5. In budgeting a property's projected income, the property manager normally makes a deduction to account for vacancies & bad debts

---

Exercise 17G

1. List the three main categories of property management functions.
   1. leasing & tenant relations
   2. mgr/owner relations
   3. property maintanence

2. The most popular method for marketing residential rental space is classified ads.

3. Of the various forms of advertising that are available to a property manager, the least cost effective is usually radio & t.v. ads.

4. Indicate whether each of the following statements is true or false.

   A lease for a term of 6 months or more must be in writing and signed by the lessor (landlord). T (F)

   When a lease expires, it is usually better to try to find a new tenant, rather than renew the expired lease, since it is easier to raise the rent for a new tenant than for an existing tenant. T (F)

   If a lease has an automatic renewal clause, it cannot be terminated by the landlord without the tenant's consent. T (F)

5. The most effective way to avoid delinquencies in rental payments is Carefful selection + qualification of tenants.

Exercise 17H

1. Match the terms on the left with the corresponding descriptions on the right.

e rent roll	a.	brief description of income and expenses
d statement of operations	b.	list of all expenses paid during a given time period
a summary of operations	c.	list of all units and their going rental rates
c rent schedule	d.	periodic report of the financial and physical condition of the property
b statement of disbursements	e.	report on collected rents

2. What is a narrative report of operations?

letter explaining various elements of operations

3. Indicate whether each of the following statements is true or false.

The property manager is responsible for deciding how frequently to report to the owner. T (F)

The best way for a property manager to report a problem with the property to the owner is in writing. T (F)

A rent roll lists only the units that are currently occupied, showing the amounts of collected and uncollected rents. T (F)

4. Which of the following items would ordinarily be shown on a statement of disbursements? (Circle all that apply.)

a. security deposits received from tenants
(b.) maintenance expenses
c. delinquent rent payments
(d.) property taxes
(e.) advertising expenses

5. A narrative report of operations is especially important in cases where income is lower than projected or expenses are higher.

Exercise 17I

1. Match the terms on the left with the corresponding description on the right.

   d preventive maintenance — a. cleaning common areas

   b corrective maintenance — b. repairing a broken window

   a housekeeping — c. remodeling a unit

   c new construction — d. repainting

2. What is the difference between preventive maintenance and corrective maintenance? maintain current condition / fix defects in property

3. List the three basic steps involved in supervising the maintenance of a managed property.

   1. inventory property's equipment & phys. elements
   2. prepare schedule of maintenance
   3. maintain records of inspection, maintenance & improvements

4. The actual maintenance activities performed for a property are normally handled by maintenance employees or independent contractors.

Lesson 17: Workbook Quiz Questions

1. A technical oversupply of property results when:
   a. there are more units than consumers
   b. consumers are unable to afford current rents
   c. there are more consumers than units
   d. None of the above

2. When occupancy rates are rising, property managers tend to:
   a. lower rents
   b. raise rents
   c. evict tenants
   d. increase advertising for rental properties

3. A property manager would likely be concerned with all of the following except:
   a. trends in family size and life styles
   b. local employment levels
   c. market rental rates
   d. local commission rates on real estate sales

4. The four basic types of income-producing properties are:
   a. retail, industrial, commercial and condominium
   b. retail, wholesale, office and industrial
   c. wholesale, manufacturing, shopping and industrial
   d. residential, office, retail and industrial

5. Which of the following properties would normally have the highest turnover rate for tenants?
   a. An apartment building
   b. A shopping mall
   c. An office tower
   d. An industrial park

6. The types of businesses operated by tenants is usually of greatest concern to a manager of:
   a. retail property
   b. office property
   c. residential property
   d. industrial property

7. In retail property rentals:
   a. the rent is often based on the amount of the tenant's income
   b. property is most commonly rented on a per unit basis
   c. the property manager usually maintains an office in the retail complex
   d. it is usually best if all tenants of the property operate similar kinds of businesses

8. A description of the duties and powers of the property manager would most likely be found in:
   a. the management plan
   b. the management agreement
   c. the management proposal
   d. the management schedule

9. A property management agreement should:
   a. describe the amount and method of payment of the manager's compensation
   b. describe the owner's goals for the property
   c. have a specified term
   d. All of the above

10. A market analysis is performed as part of a property manager's preliminary study in order to:
    a. allow the property manager to become familiar with the property to be managed
    b. assess the level of maintenance of surrounding properties
    c. determine the number of competing units available to potential renters
    d. gain an understanding of regional economic conditions

11. A property manager's preliminary study normally covers four basic areas of analysis:
    a. the region, the neighborhood, the property and the market
    b. the economy, the site, the market and occupancy rates
    c. occupancy rates, absorption rates, interest rates and property values
    d. the building, the site, the neighborhood and the city

12. A list of all the rental rates assigned to the various units in a property is called:
    a. a rent roll
    b. a rental schedule
    c. a rental list
    d. a rental budget

13. A property's debt service will affect its:
    a. gross income
    b. net income
    c. cash flow
    d. operating expenses

14. Which of the following statements best describes the relationship between a management proposal and a management plan?
    a. The management plan is put into effect by means of the management proposal
    b. The management proposal becomes the management plan when it is accepted by the property owner
    c. The management plan is always developed first, before the management proposal
    d. There is no relationship between the management plan and the management proposal

15. A property's variable expenses include:
    a. property taxes and utilities
    b. utilities and maintenance expenses
    c. maintenance expenses and insurance premiums
    d. utilities and debt service

16. A property's net income is calculated by:
    a. subtracting total operating expenses from total income
    b. subtracting total operating expenses from total operating income
    c. subtracting debt service from net operating income
    d. subtracting replacement reserves from net operating income

17. The most common form of advertising for residential rental property is:
    a. direct mail
    b. display advertising
    c. classified advertising
    d. "For Rent" signs

18. Which of the following advertising methods is generally not appropriate for a property manager to use?
    a. Direct mail
    b. Broadcast media
    c. Signs
    d. Display ads

19. A lease must be in writing if:
    a. the annual rent is greater than $10,000
    b. the property will be occupied by the tenant as his or her primary residence
    c. the term of the lease is longer than one year
    d. the tenant is an individual and not a business

20. Security deposits can be used to protect a property owner from:
    a. a tenant who defaults on the payment of rent when due
    b. damage to the rental property caused by a tenant
    c. Both of the above
    d. None of the above

21. One of the most effective ways for a property manager to avoid problems related to delinquent rental payments is:
    a. careful screening of potential tenants
    b. making sure the property is fully occupied at all times to make up for the delinquent payments
    c. establishing a policy of prompt eviction for late payment of rents
    d. shutting off the utilities when rents are not paid by the due date

22. A report listing all the units of a property and showing the amount of rent collected for each unit during a given period is called:
    a. a rental schedule
    b. a statement of operations
    c. a statement of disbursements
    d. a rent roll

23. Repairing a broken window in a building is an example of:
    a. preventive maintenance
    b. corrective maintenance
    c. housekeeping
    d. elective maintenance

24. A monthly statement of operations prepared by a property manager for a property owner would usually include a description of:
    a. all money received by the property manager in connection with the property
    b. all money paid out by the property manager in connection with the property
    c. the overall condition of the property
    d. All of the above

25. A clause in a lease stating that the lease will be automatically renewed at the end of its term unless one of the parties gives the other notice of intent to terminate the lease is called:
    a. a rollover clause
    b. a periodic renewal clause
    c. an automatic renewal clause
    d. an option clause

Lesson 18

Federal Income Taxes and Real Estate

Exercise 18A

1. Which is of more value to a taxpayer, a $1,000 tax deduction or a $1,000 tax credit, and why?

   ____

2. Indicate whether each of the following statements is true or false.

   Capital gains are given preferential treatment under the tax code, as compared to ordinary income. T F

   Long-term capital gains are taxed differently than short-term capital gains. T F

   There is a limit on the amount of capital losses that a taxpayer can deduct in any one year. T F

3. A capital asset is a piece of property that is held for:

   1. ______________________ or
   2. ______________________

4. List the three categories of losses that an individual taxpayer is entitled to deduct.

   1. ______________________
   2. ______________________
   3. ______________________

5. For tax purposes, the IRS considers income to include ______________________ ______________________.

Exercise 18B

1. Match the following terms:

___ deduction	a. held for investment purposes
___ tax credit	b. acquisition cost
___ income	c. subtracted from income before tax rate applied
___ initial basis	d. any economic benefit realized by the tax payer
___ capital asset	e. subtracted directly from taxes owed

2. The Haywards bought their house in 1990 for $162,000, plus $4,500 in closing costs, so their initial basis was $166,500. In 1992 they spent $7,000 on improvements that the IRS would regard as capital expenditures. The house is currently worth approximately $176,000. How much is the Haywards' adjusted basis in the property?

   ____

3. A gain on the sale of a property is _______________ in the year the taxpayer sells the property. The gain is ordinarily _________________ and taxed in that same year, unless a special provision of the tax code applies to the transaction.

4. To determine a taxpayer's gain on the sale of a property, subtract his or her ____________________ from the amount realized (the net sales price).

5. Indicate whether each of the following statements is true or false.

   A gain is always taxable unless it falls under a specific exception in the tax code. T F

   A loss is never deductible unless it falls under a specific exception in the tax code. T F

   Property held for personal use is considered a capital asset. T F

   An owner's initial basis is equal to the cost of acquiring the asset. T F

Exercise 18C

1. Match the following terms:

___ principal residence	a. an inventory of subdivision lots
___ personal use property	b. a cabinetmaker's shop
___ property held for the production of income	c. a rental house
___ unimproved investment property	d. only one at a time
___ property used in a trade or business	e. a second home
___ dealer property	f. vacant land

2. A sale is considered to be an installment sale if the seller/taxpayer receives ______ ________________________________ in the year the property is sold.

3. Which of the following types of properties are eligible for installment sale tax reporting. (Circle all that apply.)
   a. personal use property
   b. dealer property
   c. investment property
   d. property used in a trade or business
   e. principal residence property

4. Bert sold his home for $248,000. His adjusted basis for the home was $155,400. He paid a 6% real estate commission on the sale, and $3,320 in other closing costs. The buyer made a $25,000 downpayment, and financed the balance with an installment sales contract. Under the terms of the contract, Bert will receive $1,045.75 in principal payments and $5,954.25 in interest during the year of the sale. How much income from the sale will Bert need to report on his tax return for the year of the sale?

   ____

5. True or false? Most non-recognition provisions in the tax code simply defer recognition of gain to a later tax year, they do not exempt the gain from taxation. T F

Exercise 18D

1. The Sewalls just sold their principal residence, and they realized a $15,000 gain on the sale. In order to defer taxation of that gain, they will have to reinvest the money in a new home within ___________.

2. Maria Buenavista just sold her home, realizing a gain of $93,000 on the sale. She will be allowed to exclude that gain from her income altogether; she won't ever be required to pay taxes on it. Buenavista must be at least _____ years old.

3. Linda sold her home for $145,000, and paid selling costs of $11,000. Her adjusted basis in the home was $120,000. If she buys a replacement home for $135,000, how much of the gain on the first sale will be subject to tax?

   ____

4. Using the facts from question #3 above, what is Linda's basis in her new home?

   ____

5. Indicate whether each of the following statements is true or false.

   Any gain that is realized on an involuntary conversion is usually recognized immediately. T F

   The deferral of gain on the sale of a residence is available for any personal use property. T F

   The replacement period for avoiding tax liability on an involuntary conversion is usually longer for business or income property than it is for principal residence property. T F

Exercise 18E

1. Indicate whether each of the following statements is true or false.

   An apartment building and a vacant lot are considered like-kind property for the purposes of a tax-free exchange. T F

   A taxpayer's principal residence is not eligible for a tax-free exchange. T F

   A taxpayer is entitled to a tax-free exchange only once in a lifetime. T F

2. If a taxpayer exchanged a small commercial building for a rental house and $19,000 in cash, the cash would be referred to as _________.

3. The maximum amount of gain that can be excluded under the once-in-a-lifetime sale of principal residence exemption is ___________.

4. Clyde's property is subject to a mortgage lien in the amount of $340,000. He exchanges it for property that has a $250,000 mortgage. The reduction in Clyde's mortgage liability is known as ___________________________.

5. List three non-recognition provisions in the tax code that benefit owners of real estate.
   1. ____
   2. ____
   3. ____

Exercise 18F

1. With _________________________ deductions, the taxpayer can deduct the cost of acquiring a property over a period of years. These deductions are allowed in connection with (circle all that are correct):
   a. principal residence property
   b. property used in a trade or business
   c. property held for the production of income
   d. unimproved investment property

2. Unlike buildings, land is not ___________________, because it does not wear out.

3. The Claridges own their home. They are entitled to deduct (circle all that are correct):
   a. repair expenses
   b. general real estate taxes
   c. mortgage interest

4. List the limits on the mortgage interest deduction for personal residences:

   1. For a loan used to purchase a home: $____________

   2. For a home equity loan: $____________

   These limits refer to (circle one):

   a. the amount of interest paid

   b. the size of the loan

5. What is the difference between a repair expense and a capital expenditure, and why does it matter from a tax perspective?

   ____

   ____

Lesson 18: Workbook Quiz Questions

1. Federal income tax is:
   a. proportional
   b. regressive
   c. progressive
   d. latent

2. The IRS treats any economic benefit to a taxpayer as:
   a. assets
   b. income
   c. wealth
   d. basis

3. Tax credits are:
   a. deducted from income
   b. added to income
   c. subtracted directly from the tax owed
   d. added to the tax owed

4. A gain on the sale of an asset held for personal use or as an investment is considered a:
   a. capital expenditure
   b. capital asset
   c. capital gain
   d. tax deduction

5. A taxpayer's investment in a property is called his or her:
   a. tax bracket
   b. basis
   c. realization
   d. rollover

6. Which of the following is considered a capital expenditure?
   a. Painting the exterior of a building
   b. Replacing a broken window
   c. Adding a new room to a home
   d. Repairing roof

7. After three years of ownership, Jones added the total of her capital expenditures and subtracted her allowable depreciation to determine her:
   a. adjusted basis
   b. original basis
   c. allowable tax credits
   d. deferred gain

8. Which of the following properties can not be depreciated?
   a. Property held for production of income
   b. Property used in a trade or business
   c. Personal residence
   d. Six-unit apartment building

9. A gain is not considered taxable income until it is:
   a. deferred
   b. realized
   c. depreciated
   d. deducted

10. Which of the following is not eligible for a tax-free exchange?
    a. Subdivided land held by a developer
    b. Unimproved land
    c. Factory owned by the manufacturer
    d. Residential rental property

11. Which of the following types of property is not eligible for installment sales tax treatment?
    a. Apartment complex
    b. Personal residence
    c. Vacant land
    d. Dealer property

12. Jones sells her home for a $76,000 profit, and two months later she purchases a more expensive home. What is the tax consequence of the profit earned from the sale of the first home?

    a. It is taxed in the year received
    b. It is taxed in installments over three years
    c. The tax is deferred
    d. Profit from the sale of a personal residence is not taxable

13. Which of the following may Jones deduct from her taxable income when preparing her income tax statement?

    a. Cost of repairs to her home
    b. Cost of patio in backyard
    c. Interest paid on home mortgage
    d. Special assessments paid for new sidewalks in front of home

14. Smith trades his triplex to Jones for Jones's duplex and $10,000. The cash from Jones is called:

    a. depreciation
    b. passive income
    c. boot
    d. mortgage relief

15. Cost recovery deductions:

    a. increase basis
    b. decrease basis
    c. eliminate basis
    d. have no effect on basis

16. Jim and Carla Manto are 62 and 59 years old, respectively. They sell the home they've owned for the past 19 years and realize a $112,500 profit. What is the tax consequence of the sale?

    a. The tax is deferred indefinitely
    b. The tax is based on 33% of the profit
    c. The tax is based on 100% of the profit
    d. They can take an exclusion and pay no tax

17. A taxable gain is generally recognized in the year it is:

    a. spent
    b. realized
    c. allocated
    d. fulfilled

18. Which of the following is true?

    a. A $6,000 tax credit is of more benefit to the taxpayer than a $6,000 tax deduction
    b. A $6,000 tax deduction is of more benefit to the taxpayer than a $6,000 tax credit
    c. Tax credits and tax deductions are the same
    d. Tax credits have replaced tax deductions in modern tax law

19. Initial tax basis less cost recovery deductions equals:

    a. the tax credits
    b. the adjusted basis
    c. the taxable gain
    d. the profit on the sale

20. Which of the following represents an involuntary conversion?

    a. Sale of personal residence because of out-of-town transfer
    b. Tax-free exchange
    c. Owner receives condemnation award
    d. Three-year installment sale with a balloon payment

21. Which of the following is not depreciable property?

    a. Commercial fruit orchard
    b. Apartment building
    c. Grazing land
    d. Single-family rental dwelling

22. A second home is classified as:

    a. personal use property
    b. principal residence property
    c. dealer property
    d. unimproved investment property

23. Owens proposed a tax-deferred exchange of his home for Martin's peach orchard. Which of the following is true?

    a. Residential property can't be traded for a peach orchard because they are not "like-kind"
    b. The exchange can be made, but only if boot is included with the peach orchard
    c. The exchange can be made without any special considerations
    d. Principal residence property is not eligible for a tax-deferred exchange

24. Boot is taxed:

    a. at a higher rate than other types of gains
    b. in the year it is received
    c. at the same time the profit from the property exchanged is recognized
    d. only after the taxpayer dies

25. Real estate commissions are:

    a. capital gains
    b. passive income
    c. rollover income
    d. ordinary income

Lesson 19

Civil Rights and Fair Housing

Exercise 19A

1. The ______________________ Act of 1866 and the federal ____________ Housing Act both prohibit discrimination in real estate transactions.

2. If a court finds that someone has violated the Civil Rights Act of 1866, what steps could it take to remedy the situation?

   ____

3. Why was the Civil Right Act of 1964 largely ineffective in promoting the goal of equal housing opportunity?

   ____

4. Indicate whether each of the following statements is true or false.

   The Fair Housing Act does not prohibit discrimination in non-residential real estate transactions. T F

   The Fair Housing Act is a part of the Civil Rights Act of 1968. T F

   The Fair Housing Act prohibits discrimination in advertising, lending, brokerage, and other services in connection with certain real estate transactions. T F

5. While the Civil Rights Act of 1866 prohibits discrimination based only on race or ancestry, the Fair Housing Act prohibits discrimination based on:

   1. ____________________ 5. ____________________

   2. ____________________ 6. ____________________

   3. ____________________ 7. ____________________

   4. ____________________

Exercise 19B

1. Match each term with the appropriate example:

___ blockbusting	a. refusal to make a loan because of the racial or ethnic composition of the neighborhood in which the property is located
___ redlining	b. inducing owners to sell by predicting a change in the racial makeup of their neighborhood
___ steering	c. channeling prospective buyers or tenants to or away from particular neighborhoods based on their race, religion, national origin, etc.

2. Which of the following activities would be prohibited under the Fair Housing Act? (Circle all that apply.)
   a. Refusing to rent office space to people of a certain race
   b. Changing the terms of an apartment lease on the basis of the tenants' religion
   c. Discrimination by a commercial lender in making a housing loan
   d. Refusing to show certain houses to non-white buyers

3. An important law that helps to enforce the prohibition against redlining by institutional lenders is ______________________________.

4. Under what circumstances would a single-family home owner be exempt from the requirements of the federal Fair Housing Act in selling the home?
   1. ______________________________
   2. ______________________________
   3. ______________________________

5. The so-called "Mrs. Murphy exemption" to the federal Fair Housing Act applies to rental of a room or unit in an owner-occupied dwelling with up to ________ units.

Exercise 19C

1. The Fair Housing Act's prohibition against discrimination on the basis of familial status protects adults who live with children under ____________________.

2. An exemption from the prohibition against discrimination based on familial status applies to qualified housing for _______________ persons.

3. Indicate whether each of the following statements is true or false.

   Prohibited discrimination based on familial status includes discrimination against pregnant women. T F

   An apartment complex can legally set aside a limited number of units for adults only, provided at least 80% of the units are available to families with children. T F

   Protection for familial status under the Fair Housing Act does not apply to families with adoptive children or foster children. T F

4. In order to be able to exclude children without violating the Fair Housing Act, a property must fall into one of three categories:

   1. ____
   2. ____
   3. ____

5. For purposes of the Fair Housing Act, a handicap is defined as _______________ ____.

Exercise 19D

1. The Fair Housing Act is enforced by the Department of ______________________ ____________________________, through its Office of ______________________ ____________________________.

2. A person who wants to file a complaint under the Fair Housing Act has three options for doing so:

   1. ______________________________

   2. ______________________________

   3. ______________________________

3. Fair Housing Act complaints are sometimes referred to a state agency that deals with discrimination. In Washington, this agency is the ______________________ ______________________.

4. Indicate whether each of the following statements is true or false.

   Punitive damage awards are never available for violations of the Fair Housing Act. T F

   When a Fair Housing complaint is heard by an administrative law judge, the judge can impose a civil penalty of up to $50,000. T F

   Complaints under the Fair Housing Act must be settled by binding arbitration. T F

Exercise 19E

1. For purposes of the Equal Credit Opportunity Act, consumer credit is defined as credit that is extended to ______________________ for ______________________ ______________________ purposes.

2. Indicate whether each of the following statements is true or false.

   The ECOA prohibits lenders from discriminating on the basis that a borrower's income is derived from public assistance. T F

   The Home Mortgage Disclosure Act applies to all residential lenders. T F

   The definition of "disability" under the Americans with Disabilities Act is broader than the corresponding definition under the Fair Housing Act. T F

3. The Americans with Disabilities Act prohibits discrimination on the basis of disability in any place of ______________________.

4. Which of the following laws prohibits discrimination in lending? (Circle all that apply.)
   a. The Home Mortgage Disclosure Act
   b. The Civil Rights Act of 1968
   c. The Equal Credit Opportunity Act
   d. The Americans with Disabilities Act

5. Which of the following would be exempt from the Americans with Disabilities Act?
   a. A real estate office
   b. A private home
   c. A restaurant
   d. A bank
   e. A hospital

Exercise 19F

1. The federal and state anti-discrimination laws contain exemptions allowing real estate agents to be involved in discriminatory real estate transactions under what circumstances?

   ____

2. True or false? Certain acts that are allowed under federal law constitute illegal discrimination under Washington law. T F

3. What is the deadline for filing a complaint with the Washington Human Rights Commission for a violation of the Washington Law Against Discrimination?

   ____

4. If a real estate licensee is found to have violated a state or federal anti-discrimination law, what are the potential consequences under the licensing law?

   1. ______________________________
   2. ______________________________
   3. ______________________________
   4. ______________________________

5. True or false? Discrimination based on sex is permitted under the Washington Law Against Discrimination in the case of rental of a room in an owner-occupied dwelling. T F

Lesson 19 Workbook Quiz Questions

1. The Civil Rights Act of 1866:

   a. prohibits all racial discrimination, private or public, in the sale and rental of property
   b. prohibits any discrimination based on race or ancestry
   c. was upheld by the United States Supreme Court in 1968
   d. All of the above

2. The Federal Fair Housing Act prohibits discrimination based on any of the following factors except:

   a. national origin
   b. handicap
   c. receipt of public assistance income
   d. familial status

3. An advertisement for a condominium project that states that units in the project are available for sale to "adults only" may be in violation of:

   a. The Civil Rights Act of 1866
   b. The Civil Rights Act of 1964
   c. The Civil Rights Act of 1968
   d. All of the above

4. The Federal Fair Housing Act prohibits blockbusting, a practice also known as:

   a. panic selling
   b. steering
   c. redlining
   d. slandering

5. An owner of a single-family home who sells the home without the help of a real estate broker is exempt from the requirements of the Federal Fair Housing Act:

   a. in all cases
   b. only if the owner does not own more than three such homes
   c. only with respect to discrimination on the basis of familial status or handicap
   d. only if the owner does not own more than three such homes and the sale does not involve any discriminatory advertising

6. The Home Mortgage Disclosure Act of 1975:

   a. helps to enforce the Federal Fair Housing Act's prohibition against redlining
   b. helps to enforce the Federal Fair Housing Act's prohibition against steering
   c. requires lenders to disclose the annual percentage rate for their residential mortgage loans
   d. prohibits kickbacks and referral fees in residential loan transactions

7. Mary is renting one of the units in a duplex she owns. She will be exempt from the Federal Fair Housing Act unless:
   a. she does not occupy one of the units in the duplex
   b. she hires a real estate agent to help rent the unit
   c. she places a classified add stating that the unit is available to "women only"
   d. Any of the above conditions would prevent Mary from being exempted from the Federal Fair Housing Act

8. The Federal Fair Housing Act allows discrimination on the basis of familial status provided that:
   a. at least 50% of the units in the project are available to families with children
   b. the project was developed under a government program to assist the elderly
   c. at least 90% of the units in the project are occupied by at least one person over the age of 62
   d. at least 50% of the units in the project are occupied by at least one person over the age of 55

9. The prohibition against discrimination on the basis of handicap in the Federal Fair Housing Act would not apply to discrimination against:
   a. a chronic alcoholic
   b. a heroin addict
   c. a person diagnosed as having AIDS
   d. a person with a mental disability

10. The Federal Fair Housing Act is enforced by:
    a. the Department of Housing and Urban Development
    b. the Office of Fair Housing and Equal Opportunity
    c. the Washington Human Rights Commission
    d. All of the above

11. Broker Bill is the subject of a discrimination complaint based on the Federal Fair Housing Law. This is the first time Broker Bill has been accused of such an offense. The complaint is being litigated before an administrative law judge. If the judge finds Broker Bill guilty of violating the Act, she may:
    a. order him to pay punitive damages of up to $10,000
    b. order him to pay a civil penalty of up to $10,000
    c. order him to pay punitive damages of up to $50,000
    d. order him to pay a civil penalty of up to $50,000

12. Which of the following laws is designed to eliminate discrimination in lending activities?
    a. Federal Fair Housing Act
    b. Equal Credit Opportunity Act
    c. Home Mortgage Disclosure Act
    d. All of the above

13. Discriminatory conduct that is exempt from the Federal Fair Housing Act:
    a. is automatically exempt from any state regulations
    b. can never result in sanctions for illegal behavior
    c. may be still be illegal under the provisions of some other federal or state law
    d. is assumed to be legal unless a real estate broker is involved

14. According to the Americans With Disabilities Act:

    a. a real estate office is considered to be a public accommodation
    b. a disability is defined as any permanent physical impairment
    c. architectural barriers that prevent access to goods and services must be removed regardless of cost
    d. all multi-story buildings must be equipped with elevators

15. The Washington State agency that is responsible for enforcing anti-discrimination laws is:

    a. the Human Rights Commission
    b. the Civil Rights Commission
    c. the Civil Liberties Commission
    d. the Fair Practices Board

16. As a general rule, Washington State laws against discrimination:

    a. apply only to discrimination in housing
    b. have fewer exemptions than comparable federal laws
    c. impose stricter penalties when the discrimination involves a licensed agent
    d. have fewer protected classes of people than comparable federal laws

17. The Washington Law Against Discrimination:

    a. is essentially a fair housing law
    b. does not apply to places of public amusement such as movie theaters and sports arenas
    c. does not apply to discriminatory acts unless a licensed real estate agent is involved
    d. prohibits racially restrictive covenants in a warranty deed

18. Joan wants to rent out the spare bedroom in her house, but she is only willing to accept female tenants. Which of the following statements is true?

    a. The Washington Law Against Discrimination does not prohibit discrimination based on sex in the rental of a room in an owner-occupied dwelling
    b. Joan is technically in violation of the Washington Law Against Discrimination, but will not be prosecuted unless someone complains
    c. Joan is technically in violation of the Washington Law Against Discrimination, but the Human Rights Commission does not accept cases involving discrimination based on sex in the rental of rooms where the parties are to share living space
    d. None of the above

19. Under Washington law, a person who has been the subject of unlawful discrimination may file a complaint with the Human Rights Commission:

    a. within six months after the alleged discrimination took place
    b. within one year after the alleged discrimination took place
    c. within two years after the alleged discrimination took place
    d. within three years after the alleged discrimination took place

20. One important distinction between the Civil Rights Act of 1866 and the Federal Fair Housing Act is that:

    a. the 1866 Civil Rights Act does not apply to residential transactions
    b. the 1866 Civil Rights Act does not prohibit discrimination based on race
    c. the Fair Housing Act does not prohibit discrimination based on religion
    d. the Fair Housing Act does not apply to non-residential transactions

21. Which of the following transactions could be exempt from the Federal Fair Housing Act?
    a. Rental of a unit in a six-unit apartment building, if the owner does not reside on the property
    b. Rental of a unit in a ten-unit apartment building, if the owner occupies one of the units
    c. Sale of a single-family home by the owner, with no real estate agent involved
    d. Sale of a single-family home listed with a real estate broker

22. Which of the following is considered a handicap for the purposes of the Federal Fair Housing Act?
    a. AIDS
    b. Mental retardation
    c. Blindness
    d. All of the above

23. In 1988, the Federal Fair Housing Act was amended to prohibit discrimination based on:
    a. substance abuse or age
    b. marital status or national origin
    c. handicap or familial status
    d. handicap or occupation

24. Under the Federal Fair Housing Act, it is not illegal to refuse to sell a condominium unit to a family with children if:
    a. the condominium qualifies as housing for older persons, with a majority of the units occupied by at least one person over 55
    b. the condominium is advertised as an "Adults Only" complex
    c. the family includes one or more children under ten years old
    d. All of the above

25. Redlining refers to:
    a. channeling prospective buyers toward or away from particular areas based on their race or ancestry
    b. refusing to make loans in a particular neighborhood because of its racial or ethnic composition
    c. inducing owners to list or sell by predicting a change in the racial or ethnic composition of the neighborhood
    d. None of the above

Residential Real Estate

Exercise 20A

1. Most foundations of newer homes are made of ______________________.

2. Match the following terms.

___ stud	a. parallel roof framing member
___ rafter	b. exterior finish material
___ joist	c. covering applied to frame
___ sheathing	d. vertical wall framing member
___ siding	e. floor and ceiling frame
___ plate	f. horizontal wall framing member

3. Which of the following styles of housing is usually the least expensive to build in terms of cost per square foot?
   a. ranch
   b. split-level
   c. two story

4. Why does the electrical system of a house have circuit breakers (or fuses)?

   ____

5. A material's R-value is a measure of its ability to ______________________ ____________. If one material is a better insulator than another, it will have a (higher / lower) R-value.

6. List three methods that can be used to prevent termite infestation.

   1. ______________________________
   2. ______________________________
   3. ______________________________

Exercise 20B

1. In the long run, the monthly cost of owning a home is usually (more / less) than the cost of renting a home. Why?

   ____

2. The ability to have access to amenities that would otherwise be unaffordable is an advantage of (buying / renting).

3. List two tax advantages that tend to reduce the cost of owning a home.

   1. ______________________________
   2. ______________________________

4. Indicate whether each of the following statements is true or false.

   In the short term, renting is usually less expensive than buying a home. T F

   A home's rate of appreciation in value can have a substantial impact on the cost of ownership. T F

   A major disadvantage of buying a home instead of renting is the financial risk involved. T F

5. List two factors (other than tax advantages) which tend to make the true cost of buying a home less than the cost of the monthly mortgage payment.

   1. ______________________________
   2. ______________________________

Exercise 20C

1. Why is the percentage of home ownership in a neighborhood an important factor in choosing a home to buy?

   ____

2. List three factors that should be considered when evaluating the site of a home.

   1. ____
   2. ____
   3. ____

3. As a rule, a home should have at least two bathrooms if it has __________ or more bedrooms.

4. Which of the following are generally considered design deficiencies in a home? (Circle all that apply.)

   a. Separate dining room, with no eating area in kitchen

   b. No outside entry to basement

   c. Living room not visible from kitchen

   d. Bedrooms not visible from front entry

   e. No closet in front entry

   f. Front door opens directly into living room

5. It is usually desirable for the kitchen in a home to be located (circle all that apply):

   a. near an outside entry

   b. within sight of the family room

   c. near the garage or carport

   d. near the dining room

   e. near outdoor living areas

Exercise 20D

1. The three fundamental considerations in making any investment are ____________________, ____________________ and ________________.

2. Indicate whether each of the following statements is true or false.

   The safest investments are usually the most liquid. T F

   The most liquid investments usually have the highest yield. T F

   Real estate is considered a very liquid investment. T F

   The safety of an investment is related to the length of time that the investor can hold on to the investment. T F

3. The difference between a property's value and the amount of the liens against it is called the owner's ________________.

4. How can an investment in real estate be converted into cash without selling the property?

   ____

5. Smith's property increased in value by 5% last year, but the value of Smith's investment in the property increased by 30%. How is this possible?

   ____

6. The two ways in which a real estate investment can increase an owner's net worth are ____________________________, and ________________________________.

Lesson 20: Workbook Quiz Questions

1. The advantages of a one-story ranch style home include:
   a. maximum lot coverage in relation to square footage
   b. ease of construction and maintenance
   c. effective use of land with varying topography
   d. economical construction cost per square foot

2. In general, the most cost effective architectural style for residential construction is:
   a. ranch/rambler
   b. split level
   c. split entry
   d. two-story

3. The vast majority of modern building foundations are made out of:
   a. unreinforced concrete
   b. reinforced concrete
   c. reinforced steel
   d. stone pilings

4. The visible exterior finish material applied to the walls of a house is called:
   a. sheathing
   b. drywall
   c. siding
   d. lath

5. A load bearing wall in a house is a wall that:
   a. bears down on some other part of the building
   b. contains headers for door and window openings
   c. supports the weight of an upper floor, ceiling or roof
   d. rests directly on the foundation

6. The standard voltage for most electrical circuits in residential buildings is:
   a. 110 volts
   b. 150 volts
   c. 220 volts
   c. 250 volts

7. Which of the following is an advantage of buying a home as opposed to renting?
   a. Lower initial cash outlay
   b. Lower initial monthly payments
   c. Lower financial risk
   d. Greater privacy

8. The advantages of renting a home as opposed to buying include all of the following except:
   a. greater mobility
   b. fewer responsibilities
   c. greater security
   d. less financial commitment

9. The cost of buying a home may be substantially less than it appears at first glance, due to:
   a. the availability of tax deductions for mortgage interest
   b. the fact that part of the mortgage payment goes to repayment of the loan debt
   c. the benefits to the owner of appreciation in property values
   d. All of the above

10. A homeowner is in the 28% federal income tax bracket. His monthly loan payment includes $850 for interest, $100 for principal, $20 for insurance reserves and $150 for property tax reserves. What is the owner's net cost for the loan payment?

    a. $740
    b. $882
    c. $1,020
    d. $1,120

11. As a general rule, a house is more likely to appreciate in value if it is located:

    a. in a neighborhood with a good balance of owner-occupied and rental homes
    b. in a neighborhood with mostly owner-occupied homes
    c. in a neighborhood with mostly rental homes
    d. in a neighborhood with a mixture of homes and small businesses

12. Which of the following considerations would likely have the greatest impact on the value of homes in a neighborhood?

    a. Quality of schools
    b. Availability of cable TV service
    c. Distance to health care facilities
    d. Street patterns

13. In evaluating the condition of a home, it is usually considered an advantage if:

    a. the kitchen is located near the bedrooms
    b. the kitchen has convenient access to an outside entrance
    c. the bedrooms are located near the family room
    d. the garage is detached from the house

14. All of the following would be considered design deficiencies in a home except:

    a. front door opens directly into the living room
    b. bedrooms are visible from the foyer
    c. family room is visible from the kitchen
    d. bedrooms are not separated by closets or baths

15. The most important consideration when making an investment is:

    a. liquidity
    b. safety
    c. yield
    d. All of the above

16. In general, the safest investments:

    a. have the highest returns
    b. are backed by the government
    c. are debt investments rather than equity investments
    d. have the highest liquidity

17. The advantages of real estate as an investment include:

    a. liquidity
    b. leverage
    c. guaranteed appreciation
    d. All of the above

18. The ability to take full advantage of an investment's appreciation without having to invest the full cost of the investment is a result of:

    a. leverage
    b. cash flow
    c. yield
    d. equity

19. The difference between the value of a property and the total amount of the liens against it is called:
    a. cash flow
    b. equity
    c. appreciation
    d. loan to value ratio

20. Which of the following would not be considered an investment in real estate?
    a. Mortgage backed securities
    b. Real estate mortgage investment conduits
    c. Real estate investment trusts
    d. Mutual funds

21. Beginning real estate investors often choose to invest in residential property because:
    a. the rate of return on residential property is consistently higher than that of other types of property
    b. residential property provides more tax advantages for investors than other types of property
    c. residential property tends to be more affordable than other types of property
    d. residential property has a higher rate of appreciation than other types of property

22. A rental home will generally have more appeal if it is located near:
    a. a college or university
    b. an airport
    c. a highway
    d. an industrial area

23. The tax advantages of investing in real estate include all of the following except:
    a. deferral of gain on installment sales
    b. tax-deferred exchanges of investment property
    c. exclusion of long-term capital gains from taxation
    d. deduction of mortgage interest

24. Which of the following investments would be likely to offer the highest rate of return?
    a. A savings account
    b. A certificate of deposit
    c. A government bond
    d. Real estate

25. In wood frame construction, the parallel framing members used to support floor and ceiling loads are called:
    a. load bearing walls
    b. joists
    c. rafters
    d. beams

Real Estate Math

Exercise 21A

1. When a formula can be expressed in the form "A = B x C", how should the formula be written when "B" is the unknown quantity?

   ____

2. What is the most important step in solving any math problem?

   ____

3. How do you convert a fraction to a decimal?

   ____

4. If you multiply two numbers, each with 3 decimal places, how many decimal places will there be in the answer? _______

5. In order to multiply or divide decimal numbers on a calculator, what special steps must be taken?

   ____

Exercise 21B

1. What is the formula for the area of a:

   rectangle: ____________________________

   triangle: ____________________________

2. A rectangular building measures 24 feet by 9 yards. What is the first step in finding the area of the building?

____

3. Surveyors sometimes use a unit of measurement called a "rod". 320 rods is equal to 1 mile. How many square rods are in 1 square mile?

____

4. What is the best way to calculate the area of a figure that has an irregular shape?

____

Exercise 21C

1. What is the formula for solving percentage problems?

____

2. What is 325% of 100? _______________

3. If you knew the amount of a commission and the commission rate, how would you determine the sales price?

____

4. A $50,000 loan bears interest at the rate of 12% per year. If you want to find the amount of interest that will accrue over 6 months, what is the first step in solving the problem?

____

5. If you know the amount of interest that accrues in two years, and the annual interest rate, how can you determine the principal amount of the loan?

____

Exercise 21D

1. What is the difference between the capitalization formula and the percentage formula?

   ____

2. If you pay $1 for a lottery ticket and win $100 in the lottery, what is your profit percentage?

   ____

3. In order to determine a property's net income, what must be deducted from its gross income?

   ____

4. In order to solve a proration problem, you may need to know the number of days in the year. How can you tell whether a year has 365 days or 366 days (without looking at a calendar)?

   ____

5. Investor A is seeking a 10% rate of return, while investor B wants a 12% rate of return. Investor A will pay (more / less) than Investor B for a property with $10,000 annual net income.

Lesson 21: Workbook Quiz Questions

1. The asking price is $145,000. The property sells for $130,000. The commission is 6%. 60% of the commission goes to the broker and 40% goes to the salesperson. How much did the salesperson receive?

   a. $2,190
   b. $2,850
   c. $3,120
   d. $3,335

2. The salesperson earns a 6% commission on the first $100,000 of the sales price and 3% of that portion of the sales price that exceeds $100,000. The commission is $7,050. What is the sales price?

   a. $135,000
   b. $141,000
   c. $153,000
   d. $154,500

3. A property recently sold for $90,000. It is assessed at 25% of its value. What will the tax be if the tax rate is $5.50 per $100 of assessed valuation?

   a. $837.45
   b. $994.67
   c. $1,045.32
   d. $1,237.50

4. A parcel of land has dimensions of 2,350' by 1,845'. One-fifth of the land must be dedicated to the public for roads and an elementary school. The land that remains will be subdivided into quarter- acre lots. How many lots will be available for sale?

   a. 301
   b. 315
   c. 318.5
   d. 321.7

5. A home is presently appraised at $150,000. Calvin bought it new four years ago. Since then it has depreciated 16%. What was the home originally worth?

   a. $164,450
   b. $178,571
   c. $183,511
   d. $186,975

6. From the point of beginning, a property's boundaries run 900' in a southerly direction; then due east for 1,250 feet; then in a northerly direction 300'; then back to the point of beginning. How many square feet are in the described parcel?

   a. 750,000
   b. 775,000
   c. 800,000
   d. 805,000

7. Smith bought a home six years ago for $110,000. He wants to sell the property for a 25% profit after paying a 7% commission and $750 in settlement costs. What would he have to sell the home for?

   a. $134,500
   b. $141,216
   c. $148,656
   d. $150,090

8. The seller wants to net $89,000. She has to pay a 6% commission, $1,250 for repairs to the property, and $2,550 in settlement costs. How much must the property sell for?

   a. $93,440
   b. $94,115
   c. $94,785
   d. $98,723

9. A borrower obtains a mortgage loan in the amount of $99,000, with semi-annual interest payments of $4,331.25. What is the loan's interest rate?

   a. 8.50%
   b. 9.0%
   c. 8.75%
   d. 9.25%

10. A salesperson sells an apartment building for $2,500,000. She earns a commission of $122,500. If she was paid a 7% commission on the first $1,000,000 of the sales price, what was her rate of commission on the remaining part of the sales price?

   a. 3%
   b. 3.5%
   c. 4%
   d. 6%

11. A mortgage loan is 80% of the sales price. The loan's interest rate is 9%, and the borrower makes semi-annual interest payments of $6,750. What is the sales price?

   a. $176,000
   b. $181,250
   c. $187,500
   d. $191,450

12. The broker's commission is 7% of the sales price. What is the commission if the property sells for $3.50 per square foot and its dimensions are 200' x 175'?

   a. $8,050
   b. $8,138
   c. $8,575
   d. $9,112

13. A 10-year-old property recently appraised for $257,000. It has depreciated 25% since it was new. What was it originally worth?

   a. $342,667
   b. $355,886
   c. $356,925
   d. $392,125

14. A convenience store occupied 30% of a 150' x 200' lot. Ten percent of the lot was condemned for a public easement. How many square feet was left for parking after the easement was established?

   a. 18,000
   b. 18,460
   c. 19,759
   d. 21,346

15. A lender charges a borrower 3 points. How much money will the borrower have to have at closing if the sales price is $145,000 and the lender is requiring a 20% downpayment?

   a. $32,480
   b. $4,350
   c. $3,480
   d. $33,350

16. Jones borrowed $45,000 to purchase some office furniture. He agreed to pay 9.5% interest plus the amount borrowed at the conclusion of 20 months. What was the amount of the payment?

   a. $42,550
   b. $47,650
   c. $52,125
   d. $54,675

17. Able purchases a property for $55,000 and puts 20% down. The monthly interest payments are $375.50. What is the annual rate of interest?

    a. 9.50%
    b. 9.90%
    c. 10.10%
    d. 10.24%

18. An appraiser determines the property's net operating income is $25,750. If she applies a capitalization rate of 11.5%, what is the market value of the property?

    a. $223,913
    b. $225,674
    c. $229,580
    d. $258,748

19. A building's dimensions are 35' x 60' x 9'. How many square feet does it contain?

    a. 2,100
    b. 3,450
    c. 18,900
    d. 21,355

20. A buyer purchases a house for $75,000 with a 15% downpayment. The seller pays a 3% discount and a 1% loan origination fee on behalf of the buyer. What is the cost to the seller if she also pays a 6% commission?

    a. $6,375
    b. $7,050
    c. $7,500
    d. $8,250

21. Carla purchased a home for $155,000 and obtained an 80% loan for 30 years at 8.25% interest. Carla's monthly payment is $931.57. How much interest will Carla pay over the life of the loan?

    a. $211,365
    b. $268,679
    c. $335,365
    d. $341,444

22. Johnson, a salesperson for ABC Realty, sold a home listed by ACME Realty for $104,000. The companies split the 6% commission 50/50, and Johnson's share of her company's commission was 40%. What was the amount of Johnson's commission?

    a. $1,115
    b. $1,248
    c. $3,120
    d. $3,225

23. Able makes $1,200 quarterly interest payments on a term loan. If the interest rate is 9.5%, what is the amount of the loan?

    a. $45,060
    b. $50,526
    c. $52,221
    d. $59,788

24. A convenience store grosses $555,000 annually. Its operating expense ratio is 83%. If the appraiser assigns an 11% capitalization rate, what is the estimated value of the property?

    a. $857,727
    b. $892,345
    c. $901,211
    d. $950,445

25. A property sells for $105 per front foot. It is half an acre with a depth of 112'. What is its sales price?

    a. $19,941
    b. $20,419
    c. $21,556
    d. $23,888

Lesson 22

Washington Real Estate License Law

Exercise 22A

1. The members of the Real Estate Commission are usually real estate brokers with at least _________ years of experience.

2. The license law defines a real estate broker as a person who performs certain activities (such as selling or negotiating the sale of real estate):

   1. on behalf of another person, and
   2. ____

3. A real estate license is required not only for selling real estate, but also for selling ____, even if no real estate is involved.

4. The definition of "real estate broker" in the license law includes people who act as agents for compensation in performing any of the following activities (circle all that apply):

   a. offering to buy real estate

   b. offering to sell real estate

   c. negotiating a lease of real estate

   d. offering to negotiate a lease of real estate

   e. offering to negotiate an exchange of real estate

   f. offering to negotiate an exchange of business opportunities

5. What are the two primary purposes of the license law?

   1. ____
   2. ____

Exercise 22B

1. Eileen Harvey does not have a real estate license. Acting under a power of attorney, she is negotiating the sale of property owned by her friend, Ben Davidson. This is not a violation of the license law, as long as Harvey ____. Harvey would be referred to as Davidson's ____________________________________.

2. Larry Varjak does not have a real estate license. He is showing prospective tenants an apartment in the Claremont Arms, a building he does not own. This is not a violation of the license law (circle all that are correct):
   a. if he is the resident manager of the building, or
   b. if he has taken an approved course in property management, or
   c. if his parents own the building, or
   d. if the building has no more than six units

3. When a real estate broker's license is issued to a corporation, one of the corporate officers must be named as the firm's ___________________________ broker.

4. An associate broker (circle all that are correct):
   a. has met the qualifications for a broker's license
   b. is an affiliated licensee of a broker
   c. is licensed to represent members of the public directly, without a broker
   d. may manage a branch office of a brokerage

5. The term "affiliated licensee" refers to (circle all that are correct):
   a. brokers
   b. associate brokers
   c. salespersons
   d. designated brokers

Exercise 22C

1. Gloria Herrera just received notice that she passed the salesperson's exam. The results will be valid for ___________________________ from the exam date. If she doesn't become licensed within that period, she will have to ______________ __________________ in order to apply for a license.

2. To qualify for a broker's license, an applicant must have completed ______ clock hours of approved courses within the previous ______ years, including 30-hour courses in each of the following subjects:

   1. ______________________________
   2. ______________________________
   3. ______________________________

3. Which of the following subjects are tested on the real estate exam? (Circle all that apply.)

   a. arithmetic

   b. agency relationships

   c. real estate license law

   d. business ethics

   e. real estate economics

4. Indicate whether each of the following statements is true or false.

   The minimum age requirement for all types of real estate licenses is 18. T F

   If an applicant for a broker's license has five years' experience as a real estate appraiser, the Director of the Department of Licensing is required to waive the requirement for two years' experience as a full-time real estate salesperson. T F

   A broker who is actively licensed in Idaho is automatically eligible to take the Washington broker's exam, and does not need to satisfy the requirements for education and experience. T F

   An applicant for a salesperson license must have a high school diploma or equivalent. T F

   An applicant for a broker's license is required to have worked as a real estate salesperson at least 20 hours a week for three years or more. T F

5. Anyone who has been convicted of a crime within ten years before applying for a license (circle all that apply):
   a. must submit fingerprint identification to the Department of Licensing
   b. is prohibited from obtaining a broker license
   c. must post a $5,000 security bond in order to obtain a license
   d. must submit three character references to the Department of Licensing

Exercise 22D

1. Indicate whether each of the following statements is true or false?

   A course that a licensee took to fulfill the initial requirements for licensing can also be used to fulfill the continuing education requirements. T F

   A person with an inactive real estate license is not permitted to engage in activities that require a license, but is still subject to disciplinary action for violations of the license law. T F

   Once a real estate license is canceled, the former licensee must follow all the steps for initial licensure in order to become licensed again. T F

2. To get a real estate license renewed, the licensee must take ________ clock hours of approved continuing education courses. At least _________ of those hours must be in substantive courses.

3. James receives his first real estate license on December 31, 1995. He will be required to renew the license:
   a. on his birthday in 1996
   b. on his birthday in 1997
   c. on December 31, 1996
   d. on December 31, 1997

4. In addition to the regular continuing education requirements for license renewal, the first renewal of a salesperson's license requires completion of an approved _____ clock-hour course in ______________________________________.

5. The holder of an inactive real estate license: (circle all that apply):
   a. must renew the license by its renewal date
   b. must satisfy all the requirements for renewal of an active license in order to avoid cancellation of the license
   c. must reactivate the license within three years, or it will be canceled
   d. is required to complete additional education requirements in order to reactivate the license

Lesson 22: Workbook Quiz Questions

1. The duties of the Director of the Department of Licensing include all of the following except:
   a. holding disciplinary hearings
   b. granting or denying licenses
   c. appointing the commissioners
   d. issuing rules and regulations governing real estate licensees

2. The Department of Licensing regulates licenses for:
   a. salespersons
   b. associate brokers
   c. brokers
   d. All of the above

3. Which of the following persons is required to have a real estate license?
   a. An attorney at law, in the performance of his or her duties as a lawyer
   b. One who sells property for a family member and keeps a small percentage of the selling price as compensation
   c. A property owner who sells his or her own property
   d. An authorized attorney in fact, acting without compensation

4. A applicant for an associate broker's license must meet all of the following requirements except:
   a. he or she must be at least 18 years old
   b. he or she must have five years of recent experience in real estate work
   c. he or she must be a high school graduate
   d. he or she must pass the broker's exam

5. The real estate commissioners:
   a. serve for three years
   b. are elected from their respective congressional districts
   c. prepare and administer real estate license exams
   d. must have ten years of real estate experience

6. A real estate salesperson is:
   a. an affiliated licensee
   b. a designated broker
   c. authorized to receive a commission directly from a client
   d. None of the above

7. An applicant for a real estate license takes and passes the exam, but does not apply for his license until seven months later. The applicant:
   a. will be issued a license if he meets all of the other requirements
   b. must pay a late penalty
   c. must pay an exam fee and take the exam again
   d. must submit a new application, pay the fee, and take the exam again

8. Every applicant for an associate broker's license:
   a. must provide fingerprint identification at the time of submitting an application
   b. can work with an interim license for a maximum of 45 days
   c. must have a job lined up before submitting his or her application
   d. All of the above

9. Glenn's broker's license was first issued on March 10, 1995, and his birthday is August 26. The expiration date for his license is:
   a. March 10, 1996
   b. August 26, 1997
   c. March 10, 1997
   d. August 26, 1996

10. The continuing education requirement is:
    a. 30 hours of courses in real estate fundamentals
    b. 10 hours of approved substantive courses and 20 hours of non-substantive courses
    c. 15 hours each of approved substantive and non-substantive courses
    d. a total of 30 hours of approved courses, with at least 20 hours of substantive courses

11. Betty allowed her real estate license to expire 10 months ago. In order to engage in real estate activities, she must:
    a. apply to have her license reinstated
    b. pay a penalty in order to be able to renew her license
    c. take the license exam
    d. complete 60 clock hours of approved real estate courses

12. All of the following are exempt from the real estate licensing requirement except:
    a. A resident manager of a residential apartment complex
    b. An owner of a rental self-storage facility
    c. A professional property manager
    d. A trustee in bankruptcy

13. An attorney in fact is someone who:
    a. has passed the state bar examination
    b. has graduated from law school but does not have an attorney's license
    c. has been appointed as an agent under a written power of attorney
    d. has been appointed by a court to dispose of property

14. An applicant would be most likely to apply for an associate broker's license because he or she:
    a. did not have the required experience to obtain a broker's license
    b. wanted to work as a branch office manager for another broker
    c. was already licensed as a broker in another state
    d. wanted to open an office in another state

15. An associate broker's license may be issued to:
    a. a natural person
    b. a one-person corporation
    c. a partnership
    d. Either a) or b)

16. When a broker's license is issued to a corporation or partnership:
    a. the license names the business as the broker, and an officer or general partner as the designated broker
    b. the license names all officers or general partners of the business as designated brokers
    c. the license names an officer or general partner as broker, and the business as the designated broker
    d. the license is issued in the name of the designated broker only

17. A high school diploma or equivalent is not required in order to obtain a license as a:

    a. broker
    b. designated broker
    c. associate broker
    d. salesperson

18. Because Mark has been a real estate appraiser for 10 years, the Department of Licensing grants him a waiver from the experience requirement for a broker's license. If Mark fails to pass the broker's exam on the first try:

    a. he may reapply to take the exam after 30 days
    b. he may reapply to take the exam after completing a 30 hour course in real estate law
    c. he may reapply to take the exam after completing a 30 hour course in real estate practices
    d. he may not reapply to take the exam until he fulfills the experience requirement for a broker's license

19. Unless waived by the Director, the education requirement for a broker's license requires applicants to complete:

    a. 30 clock-hours of approved classes
    b. 60 clock-hours of approved classes
    c. 90 clock-hours of approved classes
    d. 120 clock-hours of approved classes

20. To pass the salesperson license exam, an applicant must:

    a. score at least 75% on each portion of the exam
    b. score at least 75% overall
    c. score at least 70% on each portion of the exam
    d. score at least 70% overall

21. When an applicant has been notified that she has passed the salesperson license exam:

    a. she may begin working as a real estate agent immediately
    b. she may begin working as a real estate agent as soon as her broker receives her license from the Department of Licensing
    c. she may begin working as a real estate agent after waiting at least 10 days for her broker to received her license
    d. she may begin working as a real estate agent only if she applies for an interim license

22. A broker's license issued to a corporation or partnership:

    a. requires a separate fee for the business and for the designated broker
    b. must be renewed every two years
    c. is not subject to the continuing education requirement for renewal
    d. All of the above

23. When a salesperson renews his or her license for the first time, he or she must submit proof of completion of:

    a. 30 clock hours of approved continuing education courses
    b. a 30 clock-hour course in real estate practices
    c. Both of the above
    d. None of the above

24. A license that has been canceled due to non-renewal may be reinstated within:

    a. one year of the date of cancellation
    b. one year of the date of expiration
    c. two years of the date of cancellation
    d. two years of the date of expiration

25. A licensee is required to notify the Department of Licensing if he or she:
    a. gets married
    b. gets divorced
    c. obtains a GED certificate
    d. moves

Regulation of Business Practices

Exercise 23A

1. A real estate salesperson has just violated the license law. Who in addition to the salesperson may be subject to disciplinary action as a result of this violation?

   ____

2. When a salesperson's affiliation with a particular broker is terminated, the salesperson's license must be ______________________________ .The license cannot be reactivated until the salesperson has become __________ ______________________________.

3. What is the definition of a fee broker?

   ____

4. Indicate whether each of the following statements is true or false.

   The relationship between a broker and an affiliated licensee may be terminated at any time by either party. T F

   If a salesperson has been terminated because of conduct that would be grounds for disciplinary action under the license law, the salesperson's broker is not required to surrender the salesperson's license to the Department of Licensing. T F

   A broker may be liable for harm caused by the actions of an affiliated licensee, even if the licensee's activities were in violation of the broker's written policies. T F

5. If a broker refuses to surrender the license of an affiliated licensee after termination of employment, the licensee should ____.

Exercise 23B

1. Indicate whether each of the following statements is true or false?

   A broker licensed in Washington is generally required to have an office here. T F

   A broker is not allowed to have more than two branch offices. T F

   A salesperson with at least two years' experience may manage a branch office. T F

   A salesperson is not allowed to accept compensation from anyone other than his or her own broker. T F

2. A real estate advertisement that fails to include the name of the broker is called a/an ___________________. This practice (is / is not) a violation of the license law.

3. A real estate broker may not do business under a name that (circle all that apply):
   a. is deceptively similar to that of another licensee
   b. creates the impression that the brokerage specializes in income properties
   c. creates the impression that the brokerage is a nonprofit organization
   d. would tend to mislead the public

4. Brokers who are actively licensed in another state as well as in Washington must maintain a/an _______________________________ in a Washington depository, and must keep records of their Washington transactions at a ____ in Washington.

5. When a broker has more than one office, the broker's license must be displayed at ____________________________________, and the licenses of affiliated licensees must be displayed at ____.

Exercise 23C

1. Match the following terms:

___ blind ad	a. deposits of more than $5,000
___ inactive licensee	b. must be kept for at least three years
___ fee broker	c. all deposits of $5,000 or less
___ pooled trust account	d. fails to state broker's name
___ transaction folder	e. must not engage in real estate activities
___ separate trust account	f. is violating the license law

2. Which of the following is a broker allowed to pay directly out of a trust account? (Circle all that are correct.)
   a. The broker's business expenses
   b. A commission share owed to one of the broker's affiliated licensees
   c. A commission share owed to a cooperating broker

3. Under what circumstances is a broker allowed to place funds belonging to the broker into the broker's trust account?

   ____

4. Indicate whether each of the following statements is true or false.

   A broker must maintain a separate trust account for each transaction. T F

   Transaction records must be kept for at least three years after the date of the listing agreement. T F

   Trust account records must include a separate ledger sheet for each client. T F

   It is a violation of the license law for two salespersons to split a commission, unless the split is handled by their broker(s). T F

5. As a general rule, trust funds must be deposited into the broker's trust account no later than ______________________________.

Exercise 23D

1. Claude Jansen listed his house with Hannah Cohen, a broker who is licensed as the designated broker of Cohen Realty, Inc. The sale of Jansen's house to Ken Balmer was negotiated by Suzanne Potter. Potter is a salesperson who works for Haven Real Estate, Inc. Haven Real Estate is a cooperating broker from the multiple listing service that Cohen Realty belongs to. Using this information, fill in the agency disclosure provision below, which would appear in the purchase and sale agreement between Jansen and Balmer. (Assume that there was no special written agreement between the selling agent and the seller.)

   AGENCY DISCLOSURE. At the signing of this agreement the selling agent,

   ________________________________, [insert name of selling licensee and the company name, as licensed]

   represented

   ________________________________, [insert name of seller, buyer, or both]

   and the listing agent,

   ________________________________, [insert name of listing licensee and company name, as licensed]

   represented

   ________________________________, [insert name of seller, or both seller and buyer]

   Each party signing this document confirms that prior oral and/or written disclosure of agency was provided to him/her in this transaction.

2. A selling agent will be in violation of the license law if he or she has not made an agency disclosure (in writing) to the seller before ________________________

   ______________________________.

3. As a general rule, a real estate agent who receives trust funds must deposit them in the broker's trust account by ______________________________. There are a few exceptions to that rule in connection with earnest money, however. List one of the situations in which an earnest money check would not be deposited in the broker's trust account by that deadline.

   ____

4. Indicate whether each of the following statements is true or false.

   A real estate licensee is required to give clients and customers copies of any documents they have signed at the time of signature. T F

   It is a violation of the license law to accept an earnest money deposit in the form of a promissory note. T F

   A licensee who is representing the buyer in a transaction may not receive any compensation from the seller. T F

5. When there is more than one broker involved in a transaction, who is responsible for handling the earnest money deposit in accordance with the requirements of the license law?

   ____

Exercise 23E

1. A broker is allowed to charge a separate fee for handling the closing of a transaction if (circle all that are correct):

   a. the broker is not representing either party in the transaction

   b. the broker is not receiving a commission from the seller

   c. the broker is a certified escrow agent

   d. proper disclosure has been made to all parties

   e. the broker is also an attorney

2. Indicate whether each of the following statements is true or false.

   Any violation of a state or federal antidiscrimination law is also a violation of the real estate license law. T F

   The broker is responsible for insuring that the parties to every transaction receive a complete, detailed settlement statement at closing. T F

   A property management agreement between a broker and a property owner must be in writing and must state the broker's compensation. T F

3. Which of the following items is NOT required to be included in a property management agreement between a broker and a property owner? (Circle all that apply.)
   a. the number of units or square footage in the property
   b. the frequency with which the broker must inspect the property
   c. the frequency with which the broker must provide summary statements to the owner
   d. the purposes for which the broker is authorized to collect and disburse funds

4. If someone other than the broker (such as a certified escrow agent) handles the closing for a transaction, the broker (is / is not) required to keep a copy of the settlement statement in the broker's transaction folder.

5. The license law allows a broker to close a transaction in which he or she is already representing the buyer or the seller (or both), if ______________________________ ______________________________.

Exercise 23F

1. Indicate whether each of the following statements is true or false?

   Failing to give a seller a copy of the listing agreement after it is signed is grounds for disciplinary action under the license law. T F

   The Department of Licensing cannot investigate a licensee's conduct unless it has received a formal written complaint from a member of the public. T F

   After the licensee has been notified, a disciplinary hearing can be held even if the licensee does not attend the hearing. T F

   A licensee who is being prosecuted for drunk driving is required to notify the Department of Licensing. T F

   A licensee can be fined up to $1,000 for a violation of the license law. T F

2. When the Director of the Department of Licensing issues an order directing someone to stop certain conduct that violates the real estate license law, the order is called a ______________________________.

3. The Director of the Department of Licensing is going to suspend Alan Hatter's real estate license for failure to handle a client's trust funds properly. List two other penalties that the Director could impose on Hatter.

   1. ______________________________

   2. ______________________________

4. If the Director orders a hearing in regard to an accusation of misconduct against a licensee, the licensee must be notified of the time and place of the hearing at least ___________ in advance. The licensee is also entitled to receive ___________ ______________________________ along with the notice of the hearing.

5. The deadline for filing an appeal of a disciplinary decision is ________ following the decision. A licensee who files such an appeal is required to post a bond of $________ to cover court costs in the event the judge decides against the licensee.

Lesson 23: Workbook Quiz Questions

1. When a licensed salesperson advertises his or her own property for sale, the advertisement must disclose:
   a. the name of the salesperson's broker
   b. the name of the salesperson
   c. the fact that the salesperson is a licensed real estate agent
   d. All of the above

2. Broker Susan manages an apartment complex for one of her clients. Susan must:
   a. have a written property management agreement with the client
   b. disclose to the client any relationship she may have with firms that she hires to provide services to the property
   c. keep copies for her records of all summary statements she provides to the client
   d. All of the above

3. When a licensee fails to appear at a hearing in regard to a license law violation:
   a. his or her license is automatically suspended
   b. the Director may impose a fine of up to $500
   c. the hearing will be held in the licensee's absence
   d. the hearing will be postponed for 30 days

4. A broker's trust funds must be kept in an interest bearing account unless:
   a. the parties direct the broker to place the funds in a non-interest bearing account
   b. the amount of the trust funds exceeds $5,000
   c. the broker maintains a separate trust account for each transaction
   d. the trust funds are property management trust funds

5. When may a branch office be managed by a salesperson?
   a. Never
   b. If the salesperson has at least 5 years experience
   c. If the salesperson has completed 120 clock hours of approved brokerage management courses
   d. If the salesperson is directly supervised by the broker

6. If a broker fails to return an affiliated licensee's license to the Department of Licensing following termination of employment, the licensee should:
   a. file a lawsuit to compel the broker to surrender the license
   b. notify the Department of Licensing by phone
   c. hire a lawyer to send a threatening letter to the broker
   d. notify the Department of Licensing in writing

7. The maximum number of branch offices a broker may have is:
   a. 3
   b. 5
   c. 10
   d. No limit

8. Broker George is a licensed broker in Oregon. If George wants to obtain a Washington broker's license, he will be required to:
   a. surrender his Oregon license
   b. keep records of his Washington transactions at a registered location in Washington
   c. maintain a branch office in Washington
   d. move to Washington

9. A broker may place her own funds into her real estate trust account:
   a. in order to cover bank charges such as the monthly account fee
   b. in order to prevent the account from being overdrawn
   c. for a maximum of 30 days
   d. None of the above

10. A broker may share a commission with all of the following except:
    a. any broker who is licensed in Washington
    b. any broker who is licensed in Canada
    c. any associate broker who is licensed in Washington
    d. any of the broker's affiliated licensees

11. With respect to an earnest money deposit, who is responsible for insuring that the deposit is handled in accordance with the trust fund regulations of the license law?
    a. The listing broker
    b. The selling broker
    c. Both the listing broker and the selling broker
    d. The broker who first receives the earnest money from the buyer

12. One of a broker's affiliated licensees has violated the license law. To avoid being held responsible for inadequate supervision, the broker will have to show all of the following except:
    a. the broker did not participate in the violation
    b. the broker had established reasonable procedures to verify that there was adequate supervision
    c. a branch manager, not the broker, was responsible for supervising the licensee
    d. the broker did not try to avoid learning of the violation

13. Which of the following is not required in the office of a broker licensed in Washington?
    a. The broker must provide a separate office for each affiliated licensee
    b. The office must be open to the public
    c. The office must be clearly identified by a sign
    d. The broker's license must be prominently displayed

14. It is illegal for a broker to:
    a. share office space with another business
    b. maintain an office in his or her home
    c. run a blind advertisement
    d. run another business out of the same office as his or her brokerage office

15. Which of the following is NOT true of a broker's trust account?
    a. Trust funds must be deposited in the account no later than the first banking day after receipt
    b. A broker must maintain only one trust account
    c. It must be specifically designated as a trust account
    d. It must be interest-bearing (unless it is a property management trust account)

16. A broker can disburse funds directly from a trust account to pay:
    a. the broker's business expenses, when the client owes the broker money
    b. licensing renewal fees owed to the Department of Licensing
    c. a commission share owed to an affiliated licensee
    d. a commission share owed to a cooperating broker

17. The license law requires real estate brokers to keep adequate records of their transactions:
    a. until closing
    b. for at least three years after closing
    c. for at least seven years after closing
    d. until authorized to destroy them by the Director of the Department of Licensing

18. A broker may share a commission:
    a. with any licensed broker or associate broker
    b. with any licensee who is a member of or works for a member of the same MLS
    c. with any of his or her own affiliated licensees, or with any licensed broker
    d. only with his or her own affiliated licensees

19. The selling agent is required to tell the buyer who he or she is representing:
    a. orally or in writing, before preparing an offer to purchase
    b. in writing before the buyer signs an offer to purchase
    c. orally or in writing, before presenting the offer to the seller
    d. orally or in writing, at least one week before closing

20. The license law makes the broker responsible for:
    a. ensuring that the buyer and seller receive settlement statements at closing
    b. preparing a settlement statement for each transaction
    c. closing the transaction in accordance with the Real Estate Settlement Procedures Act
    d. registering each transaction with a licensed escrow agent

21. The license law prohibits licensees from discriminating in real estate transactions, not only on the basis of race, color, creed, national origin, or sex, but also on the basis of:
    a. familial status, net worth, or credit history
    b. familial status, income, occupation, or age
    c. occupation, marital status, or handicap
    d. marital status, familial status, age, or handicap

22. If a verified written complaint is filed against a licensee, the Director of the Department of Licensing is required to:
    a. investigate the complaint
    b. issue a cease and desist order
    c. suspend the licensee's license pending investigation of the complaint
    d. revoke the licensee's license pending investigation of the complaint

23. After it has been proved in a disciplinary hearing that the accused licensee has violated the license law, the Director decides to suspend her license. The suspension takes effect:

    a. immediately, when the Director signs the order
    b. as soon as the licensee receives the Director's order
    c. ten days after the Director's order is mailed to the licensee
    d. thirty days after the Director's order is mailed to the licensee

24. A licensee who is acting as the buyer's agent in a transaction:

    a. is not allowed to accept any compensation from the seller
    b. is not allowed to accept any compensation from the buyer
    c. will be regarded as a dual agent if he or she accepts part of the listing broker's commission or any other compensation from the seller
    d. can accept a share of the listing broker's commission without creating an agency relationship with the seller

25. A civil judgment has been entered against a real estate licensee. The licensee is:

    a. required to notify the Department of Licensing by the end of the next business day
    b. required to notify the Department of Licensing within 20 days if the case involved the licensee's real estate or business activities
    c. required to notify the Department of Licensing within 30 days, no matter what the case concerned
    d. not required to notify the Department of Licensing, since this is not a criminal charge

Exercise Answer Key

Exercise 1A

1. a real estate broker
2. a
3. a commission; a percentage of the sales price
4. true; false; false
5. listing the property for sale

Exercise 1B

1. attorneys, lenders, financial consultants, accountants, contractors, building/pest inspectors, contractors, architects, surveyors, appraisers, etc.
2. false; true; true
3. access to a multiple listing service
4. to help set the listing price; to gain access to a MLS; to help negotiate the sale; to help with closing; to help prepare the home for showing; to advertise and show the property; to help prepare the paperwork involved in a sale, etc.
5. too high: buyer's who are shopping in the seller's price range will not make offers, since other comparably priced properties will be more attractive; buyer's who are shopping in a lower price range may not even bother to view the property

   too low: buyer's do not normally offer more than the listing price, so the seller is likely to receive less than the property is worth

Exercise 1C

1. residential; buying
2. BENEFITS SELLER: a, b, c, d, e, f, g

   BENEFITS BUYER: b, c, d, e, g
3. false; true; false
4. b, c

Exercise 1D

1. b (The other agent's may be entitled to a commission split with the listing broker.)
2. The status of an agent as an employee or an independent contractor affects liability for certain taxes, and the need for the employer to withhold taxes from the agent's compensation.

3. 1. substantially all of the salesperson's compensation is based on commissions rather than hours worked
   2. the written employment agreement between the salesperson and his or her broker states that the salesperson will be treated as an independent contractor for federal tax purposes
4. $3,000; $1,500
5. false; true; false

Exercise 1E

1. the rate of inflation; interest rates
2. Agent's are usually paid strictly by commission, which does not become due until a sale closes.
3. agents are generally expected to generate their own business
4. High inflation may generate urgency in buyers who think prices will only increase if they wait to buy. On the other hand, high inflation tends to push up interest rates and make homes less affordable.
5. false; false; true; true

Exercise 1F

1. the public; their salespeople
2. 1. training
   2. support staff and services
   3. commission splits
   4. MLS membership
   5. affiliation with trade associations
3. false; false; false; false
4. 1. by specializing in a particular type of property
   2. by specializing as seller agents or buyer agents
   3. by offering ancillary services such as property management or escrow
5. fewer

Exercise 1G

1. apartments; commercial lots; ranches; warehouses; industrial properties; shopping centers; medical complexes; etc.
2. apartment buildings
3. true; false; true
4. the listing agent receives a commission regardless of who finds a buyer for the property

Exercise 1H

1. resident manager: lives on the premises of the managed property

   property supervisor: directly manages several properties

   regional manager: supervises several property supervisors
2. a, b, c
3. listing properties for sale or lease (residential, commercial, industrial, agricultural, etc); selling or leasing properties (various types); property management; real estate business management; assistant or transaction coordinator for another real estate agent, etc.

Exercise 1I

1. real estate brokerage
2. true; false; false; true

3. e. real estate brokerage
   c. property management
   b. appraisal
   g. investment counseling
   a. escrow
   f. title insurance
   d. land development
   i. home inspection
   h. real estate education

Exercise 1J

1. 1. to establish basic requirements (such as education and experience) for licensees
   2. to regulate the day-to-day business activities of licensees
2. the Department of Licensing
3. 1. license suspension
   2. license revocation
   3. civil lawsuit
   4. criminal prosecution
4. He or she may not engage in any further real estate activities until the fund is reimbursed.
5. fair housing and anti-discrimination agencies; land use and environmental protection agencies; agencies governing subdivisions and real estate securities; consumer protection and anti-trust agencies; etc
6. National Association of Realtors (NAR); Washington Association of Realtors (WAR)
7. 7 (the Director of the DOL and 6 Commissioners)
8. education and training; knowledge about real estate; financial security; integrity; independent worker; hard worker; enjoys people; active listener; emotionally tough

Exercise 2A

1. incidental or appurtenant
2. chattels
3. bundle of rights
4. a

Exercise 2B

1. b
2. capture
3. b
4. false
5. riparian
6. littoral
7. appropriation permit
8. b
9. zoning

Exercise 2C

1. natural
2. doctrine of emblements
3. a
4. personal property
5. personal property
6. immovable; movable
7. constructively severed

Exercise 2D

1. trade fixtures
2. b

3. 1. method of attachment
   2. intention of installer
   3. adaptation to realty
   4. relationship of the parties
   5. written agreement

4. a, b, e, g

Exercise 2E

1. it is permanently attached to the land
2. is not
3. true; false; false; false
4. 1. all items that are real property are normally included in the sale of real estate, while items that are personal property are not
   2. real and personal property are subject to differing types and levels of taxation
   3. a real estate license is required in order to act as an agent in a sale of real property

Exercise 2F

1. estate
2. 1. freehold
   2. leasehold
3. c
4. qualified fee (or fee simple conditional)
5. 1. fee simple estate
   2. life estate
6. fee simple absolute
7. measuring life
8. b
9. b
10. grantor
    life tenant
    measuring life
    remainderman
11. waste

Exercise 2G

1. leasehold
2. lease
3. lessor; lessee
4. b. Estate for years
   d. Periodic estate
   a. Estate at will
   c. Tenancy at sufferance
5. a
6. assignment

Exercise 2H

1. c
2. estate for years
3. b
4. b
5. wear and tear
6. 14

Exercise 2I

1. primary
2. c. Assignment
   a. Sublease
   b. Surrender
   d. Novation
3. yes

Exercise 2J

1. 1. surrender
   2. breach of implied covenant of quiet enjoyment
   3. breach of implied warranty of habitability
   4. failure to pay rent
   5. illegal or unauthorized use
   6. destruction of premises
   7. condemnation
2. quiet enjoyment
3. Actual
4. Constructive
5. a
6. unlawful detainer
7. d. Writ of possesion
   c. Covenant of quiet enjoyment
   a. Unlawful detainer action
   b. Warranty of habitability
8. terminates

Exercise 2K

1. c. Gross lease
   a. Graduated lease
   e. Percentage lease
   d. Net lease
   b. Ground lease
2. fixed lease
3. retail business
4. graduated lease

Exercise 3A

1. severalty
2. joint tenancy
3. joint tenancy
   1. interest
   2. title
   3. time
   4. possession
4. tenants in common

Exercise 3B

1. 1. joint tenancy
   2. community property
   3. tenancy in common
   4. tenancy in partnership
2. c. joint tenancy
   d. Community property
   b. Severalty
   a. Tenancy in common
3. b
4. Joint tenancy
5. separate property

Exercise 3C

1. c. General partnership
   d. REIT
   a. Joint venture
   b. Limited partnership
   e. Corporation
2. b
3. a corporation
4. stockholders; board of directors; officers
5. b

Exercise 3D

1. in severalty; tenant in common

2. true; false; true; false
3. Since a cooperative is owned by a single corporate entity, failure of one tenant to pay his or her share of the taxes, property mortgage, or other expenses affects the interests of all the other members of the cooperative.
4. false; false; true
5. a (A corporation usually owns the project in severalty, and the units are leased to the shareholders.)

Exercise 3E

1. nonpossessory
2. security
3. b, d
4. voluntary; specific
5. all

Exercise 3F

1. a. i, s
   b. i, g
   c. v, s
   d. i, s
   e. i, g
   f. v, s
2. the borrower is the trustor or grantor; the lender is the beneficiary
3. foreclosure
4. mechanic's (also, materialman's)
5. judgment

Exercise 3G

1. position
2. recording
3. property tax liens; special assessment liens
4. the claimant's work

Exercise 3H

1. true
2. c, d, e, f
3. six months; Declaration of Non-Abandonment of Homestead

Exercise 3I

1. e. easement in gross
   d. dominant tenant
   a. easement appurtenant
   b. servient tenement
   c. a type of easement in gross that can be assigned
2. use; exclusive possession
3. in gross
4. true

Exercise 3J

1. d. express grant
   a. express reservation
   e. implication
   c. prescription
   b. condemnation
2. grantor (servient tenant)
3. reasonably necessary; prior use
4. exclusive use
5. false (A grant of easement should be recorded to provide constructive notice to subsequent purchasers of the servient tenement.)

Exercise 3K

1. c. release
   b. merger
   a. failure of purpose
   d. abandonment
   e. prescription
2. is not
3. adverse possession
4. c
5. Nothing. (Non-commercial easements in gross normally terminate on the death of the dominant tenant, but are not affected by transfer of the servient tenement.)

Exercise 3L

1. remove something
2. a, b
3. run
4. Those who benefit from the restrictions are responsible for seeing that they are enforced, by taking legal action if necessary. Failure to take action to stop a violation of a private restriction may result in the restriction becoming unenforceable.
5. Private restrictions can enhance property values (and the therefore the developer's profit) by insuring that all properties in a neighborhood will be developed in a compatible manner and by prohibiting activities (such as nuisances) that would tend to drive down values.
6. covenant; condition

Exercise 3M

1. e. license
   c. declaration of restrictions
   b. forfeiture of title
   d. injunction
   a. encroachment
2. Easement: a, b, e, g
   License: c, d, f
3. is not; are not
4. Financial encumbrances affect title only, while non-financial encumbrances also affect the use of the property.
5. An estate is (or may become) possessory, entitling the holder to exclusive use and possession of the property. Encumbrances are non-possessory interests in real estate.
6. false; false; false; true

Exercise 4A

1. health; safety
2. state
3. b, c, e, g
4. comprehensive plans, zoning ordinances, building codes, subdivision regulations, environmental laws, etc.

Exercise 4B

1. 1. to concentrate new development in existing urban areas
   2. to ensure the adequacy of infrastructure
   3. to protect the environment and natural resources
   4. to coordinate planning among neighboring jurisdictions

2. to develop a long-range plan (general plan or master plan) for development in an area
3. true; true; false; true
4. 1. residential
   2. commercial
   3. industrial
   4. agricultural
5. floor area ratio (FAR) method

Exercise 4C

1. a. rezone
   b. variance
   d. nonconforming use
   c. conditional use
2. false
3. expanded; resumed after abandonment or destruction of the property
4. schools, churches, hospitals, cemeteries, public utility structures, etc.
5. true; false; true

Exercise 4D

1. c. plat map
   d. subdivision
   a. building permit
   b. certificate of occupancy
2. consumer
3. interstate
4. a, d, f

Exercise 4E

1. b. NEPA
   a. SEPA
   d. Shoreline Management Act
   c. environmental impact statement
2. 200 feet; 20 acres; 20 cubic feet per second
3. All are subject to SEPA.
4. true

Exercise 4F

1. 1. police power
   2. power of eminent domain
   3. power to tax
2. a, d, f
3. value
4. assessment
5. e. taxes are based on value as of this date
   c. payment of first half of taxes due
   b. physical appraisal
   a. assessment
   d. payment of second half of taxes due
6. tax rate
7. b: creates a lien
   s: a one-time charge
   g: all property within taxing district is taxed
   g: amount of taxes is based on value of property
   s: also known as improvement tax
   s: amount assessed is based on benefit received
8. excise; seller

Exercise 5A

1. express; bilateral; executory
2. unilateral
3. both parties have fully performed

4. an agreement between two or more competent persons to do or not to do certain things in exchange for consideration
5. false; false; false

Exercise 5B

1. 1. 18 years old or older
   2. mentally competent
2. voidable
3. void
4. voidable
5. legal guardian
6. offer and acceptance

Exercise 5C

1. it is accepted
2. a, b, c, d
3. counteroffer (or qualified acceptance)
4. b
5. b. actual fraud
   d. constructive fraud
   a. undue influence
   c. duress

Exercise 5D

1. 1. capacity
   2. mutual consent
   3. lawful objective
   4. consideration
2. they are in writing and signed
3. g. illusory contract
   d. constructive fraud
   f. counteroffer
   e. duress
   a. actual fraud
   c. consideration
   b. statute of frauds
4. false; false; true
5. void

Exercise 5E

1. voidable
2. VOID: b, d
   VOIDABLE: a, e
   UNENFORCEABLE: c
3. 1. one party has a voidable contract
   2. the contents of the contract can't be proven
   3. the statute of limitations has expired
4. 6 years; 3 years
5. when the contract is breached

Exercise 5F

1. full performance; cancellation; rescission; novation; accord and satisfaction (assignment does not discharge a contract, since the assignor remains secondarily liable for performance)
2. rescission; cancellation
3. secondarily
4. false
5. Accord is an agreement to accept something different from the original consideration in a contract. Satisfaction is the performance of the substituted obligation.

Exercise 5G

1. damages
2. specific performance
3. liquidated damages
4. Damages is an amount that a court orders a breaching party to pay to the other party. Liquidated damages is an amount that the parties agree in advance will be considered fair compensation for a breach of contract.
5. false; false; true

Exercise 5H

1. d. specific performance
   f. liquidated damages
   c. breach
   e. damages
   a. rescission
   b. tender
2. tender
3. when the contract has been discharged by means other than full performance (such as an accord and satisfaction), or when there is a legal excuse for non-performance (such as non-performance of an unlawful provision in the contract)

Exercise 5I

1. a, b, d
2. a, c
3. 1. The statute of frauds requires listing agreements to be in writing
   2. A broker cannot sue for a commission unless he or she has a written employment contract (listing).
4. vendee; vendor; the contract is fully executed
5. 1. serves as a receipt for the buyer's earnest money
   2. becomes the contract of sale when accepted by the seller
   3. provides for payment of the brokerage fee by the seller
6. a. broker and seller
   b. buyer and seller
   c. landlord (lessor) and tenant (lessee)
   d. escrow agent and buyer and/or seller
   e. optionor and optionee

Exercise 6A

1. b. principal
   a. agent
2. b. principal
   c. agent
   a. third party
3. b. universal agent
   c. general agent
   a. special agent
4. true
5. c

Exercise 6B

1. true
2. a, e, f
3. false
4. When the agent enters into a listing agreement with the seller.
5. When there is a written agreement to the contrary.

Exercise 6C

1. authority
2. All are included.
3. implied actual authority
4. false; false; true

Exercise 6D

1. real estate agency law
2. c. reasonable care and skill
   d. honesty and good faith
   a. accounting
   e. agency disclosure
   b. disclosure of material facts
3. a, d
4. false
5. To prevent confusion among buyers and sellers as to which parties the agents in a transaction are representing.
6. seller; reasonably reliable source

Exercise 6E

1. 1. loyalty
   2. disclose conflicts of interest
   3. suggest expert advice
   4. confidentiality
   5. good faith and continuous effort
2. 1. liability for damages
   2. loss of the agent's commission
   3. loss of any secret profits
   4. disciplinary action by the Department of Licensing
3. Sharon has an obligation to present all offers to the seller, but must also inform the seller that she is related to the person making the offer.
4. false; false; false
5. b (Specific performance is usually not available as a remedy for breach of a personal services contract, and is never available as a remedy for a tort.)

Exercise 6F

1. d. an agent's puffing
   a. duty of honesty and good faith
   c. tort
   b. material fact
2. law
3. No
4. 1. The principal participated in or authorized the act.
   2. The principal benefited from the act and the injured party is unlikely to be able to recover damages from the agent.
5. This rule states that by negotiating with third parties on behalf of a principal, the agent warrants that she is authorized to represent the principal, but not that the principal is capable of performing any agreement that may be reached.

Exercise 6G

1. b, d, e
2. false
3. The seller will be liable, provided she knew or should have known that the property was in a flood hazard zone.

Exercise 6H

1. 1. agreement
   2. principal
   3. agent
   4. expiration
2. contract
3. true
4. Acts of the Parties: e, f, g
   Operation of Law: a, b, c, d
5. 1. on completion of performance
   2. on expiration of the agency term
   3. by mutual consent

Exercise 7A

1. Inadvertent dual agency is a type of dual agency that is created accidentally, without full disclosure to both parties.
2. 1. listing broker
   2. listing salesperson
   3. selling broker
   4. selling salesperson
3. Agent - someone who is authorized to represent another (the principal) in dealings with third parties

   Listing Broker - the broker who employs the salesperson who takes the listing on a property

   Selling Broker - the broker who employs the salesperson who finds a buyer for a property

   Cooperating Broker - a broker who attempts to find a buyer for a property that is listed by a different broker
4. b. in-house sale
   c. client
   d. selling salesperson
   e. customer
   a. cooperative sale

Exercise 7B

1. If an agency relationship exists, the agent owes special duties to the party that would not otherwise be owed.
2. Buyers and sellers need to know the extent to which they can rely on a real estate agent to look out for their best interests. Agents need to avoid lawsuits and disciplinary actions for misconduct.
3. unilateral offer of subagency; cooperation and compensation
4. b
5. buyer; written agreement

Exercise 7C

1. 1. seller agency
   2. buyer agency
   3. dual agency
   4. non-agency
2. entering into a listing agreement
3. showing properties; providing information about properties; preparing offers to purchase; presenting offers to the seller; assisting in arranging financing; etc.
4. Because the services are in the best interests of the seller if they help to market the property effectively.
5. a, c

Exercise 7D

1. begins providing services to the buyer; a buyer representation agreement
2. 1. the term of the agreement
   2. a description of the type of property the buyer is interested in
   3. the price range the buyer is shopping in
   4. the conditions under which the agent will earn a fee
   5. who is responsible for paying the agent's fee
   6. a description of the agent's duties to the buyer
3. The fact that the agent owes the buyer agency duties (especially those of confidentiality and loyalty).
4. Buyer's agents who have entered into representation agreements may be compensated even if the sale involves unlisted property, so they are more likely to pursue such properties on behalf of the buyer.

Exercise 7E

1. If the buyer's agent's commission is simply a split of the commission the seller has already agreed to pay under the terms of the listing, then the cost to the seller is no greater than if the property had been sold through a broker who was acting as a seller's agent.
2. true; true; false
3. To be assured of payment if the buyer chooses to purchase an unlisted property.
4. commission split; listing agreements
5. 1. an hourly fee
   2. a commission
   3. a flat fee

Exercise 7F

1. It is impossible for an agent to fully represent both the buyer and the seller in a transaction without a conflict of interest.
2. Dual agency is most often created when there is an in-house sale. The listing salesperson represents the seller, the selling salesperson represents the buyer, and the broker represents both.
3. false; true; false
4. the informed written consent of both parties
5. non-agency; general licensee duties

Exercise 7G

1. true; true; true
2. 1. the agent must give the parties the agency law pamphlet
   2. the agent must disclose to both parties that he or she will be acting as a dual agent
   3. the agent must disclose the terms of his or her compensation
   4. the parties must sign the disclosure statement in the purchase and sale agreement
3. d

Exercise 7H

1. the Sherman Act
2. 1. price fixing
   2. group boycotts
   3. tie-in arrangements
3. b, d
4. any agreement among two or more brokers to exclude another broker from fair participation in real estate activities
5. false

Exercise 8A

1. a. patent
   b. deed
   c. will
   d. dedication
2. patent
3. c
4. a

Exercise 8B

1. a. general warranty deed
   b. special warranty deed
   c. quitclaim deed
2. b. warranty deed
   a. quitclaim deed
   c. special warranty deed
3. false (A warranty deed (general or special) transfers the after-acquired title of the grantor.)

Exercise 8C

1. c
2. true
3. power of attorney
4. statute of frauds
5. 1. acknowledgment
   2. delivery
   3. acceptance
6. deed; grantee

Exercise 8D

1. b
2. consideration
3. alienation
4. true
5. Rachel - testator
   house - devise
   cars - bequest
   sister - executor

Exercise 8E

1. d
2. intestate
3. c
4. Constitution
5. a, d
6. true
7. true

Exercise 8F

1. 1. quiet title action
   2. partition action
   3. foreclosure action
2. b
3. partition

Exercise 8G

1. 1. actual
   2. open and notorious
   3. hostile
   4. exclusive
   5. continuous and uninterrupted
2. true
3. deed
4. ten
5. tacking
6. false

Exercise 8H

1. b. alluvion
   c. avulsion
   a. accession
   d. reliction
2. accession
3. false; false; false

Exercise 8I

1. acknowledged
2. c
3. grantor; grantee
4. searches; chain
5. false
6. b
7. Lila

Exercise 8J

1. b
2. title search; title report
3. 1. standard coverage
   2. extended coverage
4. d
5. false
6. a, c
7. extended coverage
8. a

Exercise 8K

1. 1. metes and bounds
   2. rectangular (or government) survey
   3. lot and block (or platting)
2. 1. monuments
   2. courses
   3. distances
3. Monuments: oak tree; Smith Creek
   Courses: due west; S 15° E
   Distances: 430 feet; to the center of Smith Creek

Exercise 8L

1. 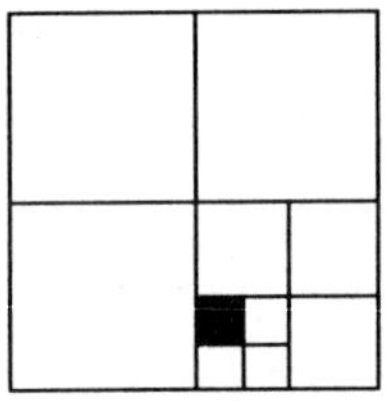

2. 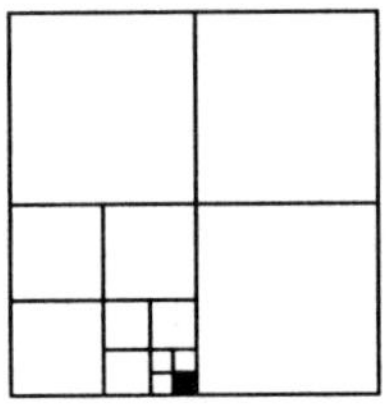

3. government lots
4. Willamette Meridian

Exercise 8M

1. plat map
2. plat map
3. e. plat map
   c. principal meridian
   f. used in rural areas
   a. sections
   d. monument
   b. township
3. lot and block system (platting)

Exercise 9A

1. listing
2. true
3. agent; principal
4. c, d, e
5. ready; willing; able
6. is
7. true
8. owes

Exercise 9B

1. open listing: a, b, e
   exclusive agency listing: f
   exclusive right to sell listing: c, d
2. open listing
3. true
4. is not
5. a, b
6. implied

Exercise 9C

1. identify
   compensate
   in writing; seller
2. legal description
3. net; unenforceable
4. 1. property description and list of features
   2. grant of authority for broker to act as seller's agent
   3. seller's agreement to pay broker's commission
   4. terms of sale acceptable to seller
   5. conditions broker must meet to earn commission
   6. seller's warranties of accuracy of information
   7. duration of listing agreement
5. are

Exercise 9D

1. closing
2. selling; commission
3. keybox

Exercise 9E

1. antitrust
2. to prevent the seller from avoiding liability for a commission by simply waiting to sell until the term of the listing agreement expires
3. 1. buyers who actually negotiated with the broker or the broker's agents
   2. buyers who first learned about the property in any way connected with the broker or the broker's agents
4. a list of the names of prospective buyers who had contact with the broker or the broker's agents during the listing period
5. 1. the broker (or some other agent) finds a ready, willing and able buyer during the listing period
   2. the seller contracts to sell or exchange the property during the listing period
   3. the seller sells the property during the extender period to a buyer who is covered by the extender clause

Exercise 9F

1. lease
2. broker's commission
3. c. seller's warranties
   a. FHA/VA loan costs
   b. hold harmless agreement
4. losing
5. seller

Exercise 9G

1. All of the parties listed should sign the listing agreement.
2. required
3. The salesperson should write his or her broker's name on the "Agent" line, and sign his or her own name on the "By" line.

Exercise 9H

1. residential property with up to four units; 5 days; the parties agree to a different deadline; the buyer expressly waives the right to receive the statement; three business days
2. false; false; false; true
3. The buyer is entitled to rescind the contract at any time prior to the closing.
4. 1. The seller can provide the buyer with an amended disclosure statement.
   2. The seller can take whatever corrective steps are necessary to restore the accuracy of the original disclosure statement.
5. true; false; false

Exercise 10A

1. b, c, d
2. b
3. a
4. 1. a promise by the buyer to pay the agreed price
   2. a promise by the seller to transfer title
5. false
6. b

Exercise 10B

1. all of it
2. false
3. The agreement may be unenforceable, and the agent who prepared it may be liable for civil damages and subject to disciplinary action by the Department of Licensing.
4. Attach the full property description to the agreement and write "See Attachment" on the form in the space provided for the description.
5. true; false; true
6. fixtures

Exercise 10C

1. b. financing
   d. closing
   f. attachment with legal description
   e. earnest money deposit
   c. included items provision
   a. extension agreement
2. lender
3. c
4. general warranty deed
5. time is of the essence

Exercise 10D

1. b
2. false
3. purchase and sale agreement
4. to the seller before the seller signs an offer to purchase, and to the buyer before the buyer signs the offer

Exercise 10E

1. community
2. the agent who receives the earnest money on behalf of the seller
3. b
4. false; false; false; false
5. b, c

Exercise 10F

1. financing
2. good faith
3. false
4. 1. a clear statement of the condition and what must be done to satisfy it
   2. the procedure for giving notice of satisfaction or waiver of the condition
   3. a deadline for satisfaction or waiver
   4. the consequences if the condition is not satisfied or waived by the deadline
5. the party who benefits from the contingency

Exercise 10G

1. FHA/VA
2. bump
3. objective
4. 1. the loan amount
   2. the loan term
   3. the interest rate
   4. the amortization period
   5. who is responsible for paying the loan costs

5. There is an inherent conflict because the contingency is not required to be satisfied or waived until after the specified closing date.

Exercise 11A

1. 1. farming
   2. cold calling
   3. contacting sellers whose listings have expired
   4. contacting owners of "for sale by owner" properties
   5. referrals
2. attorneys, accountants, bankers, escrow officers, previous clients, previous customers, etc.
3. 1. the diversity of properties in the area
   2. the agent's affinity for the area
   3. the rate of ownership turnover in the area
4. false; false; true
5. one-party listing

Exercise 11B

1. help the seller set a realistic asking price for the property
2. the prices of homes that are currently for sale; the prices of homes that have recently sold
3. Most sellers are interested in knowing how much money they will receive from the sale of their property.
4. true; false; true

Exercise 11C

1. submitting the listing to a multiple listing service
2. 1. the amount of the downpayment
   2. the amount of any payment
   3. the number of payments
   4. the period of repayment
   5. the amount of any finance charge
3. Open houses are a good way to meet potential clients and customers.
4. true; true; false
5. to keep a record of who viewed the property; to use as a source of leads for listings; and as a security measure

Exercise 11D

1. prequalifying the buyer
2. b. first-time buyer
   d. trade-up buyer
   c. empty-nester
   a. retiree
3. true; false; false
4. floor duty
5. advertising; open houses; for sale signs; checking lists of people who contact the Chamber of Commerce; working with large companies that have employee relocation needs; etc.

Exercise 11E

1. price; closing date; included items; financing terms
2. The check is usually held uncashed until the seller accepts the offer.
3. a
4. true; true; false
5. b

Exercise 12A

1. 1. the discount rate
   2. reserve requirements
   3. open market operations
2. d. open market operations
   e. federal deficit
   b. monetary policy
   c. discount rate
   a. fiscal policy
3. a, b

   (Raising and lowering the discount rate affects market interest rates, not the money supply. The Fed does not have the power to increase or decrease the federal deficit; the deficit increases or decreases in response to changes in fiscal policy.)
4. stimulate
5. the United States Treasury; government borrowing competes with private industry for available funds in the market

Exercise 12B

1. primary
2. make; borrowers; sell; investors
3. sell some mortgage loans
4. uniform underwriting standards
5. the savings of individuals and businesses in the local community

Exercise 12C

1. b. real estate cycles
   e. primary market
   d. uniform standards
   a. secondary market
   c. Fannie Mae
2. 1. Fannie Mae (the Federal National Mortgage Association)
   2. Freddie Mac (the Federal Home Loan Mortgage Corporation)
   3. Ginnie Mae (the Government National Mortgage Association)
3. true; true; true
4. GNMA
5. the Department of Housing and Urban Development (HUD)

Exercise 12D

1. 1. savings and loans
   2. commercial banks
   3. savings banks
   4. mortgage companies

   Mmrtgage companies
2. savings and loan crisis
3. loan correspondent
4. seller financing
5. false; false; false; false

Exercise 12E

1. b, c
2. a, c
3. e. consumer loan
   b. APR
   d. disclosure statement
   a. total finance charge
   c. Regulation Z
4. annual percentage rate (APR)

5. 1. the total amount financed
   2. the total of all payments for the loan
   3. the payment schedule
   4. the total number of payments
   5. whether the loan is assumable
   6. any balloon payments, late fees or prepayment charges
   7. the total finance charge
   8. the annual percentage rate (APR)

Exercise 12F

1. endorsing
2. 1. the amount borrowed
   2. the interest rate, and whether it is fixed or variable
   3. the amount of the payments
   4. when and how payments must be made
3. a straight note
4. The note is to be repaid in equal installments that are sufficient to pay both the interest and the entire principal balance by the conclusion of the loan term.
5. false; false; true; false

Exercise 12G

1. e. security instrument
   d. negotiable instrument
   a. holder in due course
   c. maker
   b. straight note
2. a
3. foreclose on the property
4. BORROWER: maker, mortgagor, trustor
   LENDER: payee, mortgagee, beneficiary
5. false; true; false

Exercise 12H

1. acceleration
2. assume; subject to; alienation (or due-on-sale)
3. a, b
4. It prohibits prepayment of principal during a part (or all) of the loan term.
5. false; true; false

Exercise 12I

1. d. alienation clause
   a. assumption
   e. subordination clause
   b. lock-in clause
   c. satisfaction
2. mortgagor (borrower); deficiency judgment
3. equitable redemption; statutory redemption
4. a satisfaction of mortgage; a deed of reconveyance
5. false; true; true

Exercise 12J

1. MORTGAGE: judicial foreclosure, statutory redemption, sheriff's sale, deficiency judgment
   DEED OF TRUST: non-judicial foreclosure, cure and reinstatement, trustee's sale, power of sale clause

2. the delinquent amount and costs incurred by the lender
3. 11 days before the scheduled trustee's sale
4. 120 days (30 days notice of default and 90 days notice of sale)
5. Advantages: can be foreclosed without going to court, and no redemption period after the sale

   Disadvantage: no deficiency judgment allowed

Exercise 12K

1. c. conventional loan
   e. blanket mortgage
   f. budget mortgage
   a. purchase money mortgage
   d. junior mortgage
   b. participation mortgage
2. interim; take-out
3. false (A wraparound buyer takes title subject to the underlying loan.); true; true
4. 1. any mortgage loan used to buy property
   2. a mortgage loan made by the seller to the buyer
5. true; false; true

Exercise 12L

1. vendee

   equitable title

   paid off the contract price

   forfeiture
2. 1. fixed disbursement plan
   2. voucher system
   3. warrant system
3. the vendee
4. 90 days
5. true; false; true

Exercise 13A

1. would sell for enough at a foreclosure sale to pay off the loan (in case of default)
2. 1. income
   2. net worth
   3. credit history
3. quantity; quality; durability
4. two years
5. false; false; true

Exercise 13B

1. 1. send an income verification form directly to the employer
   2. obtain copies of the applicant's W-2 forms for the past two years, and pay stubs for the previous month, and verify with the employer by phone
2. whether the payments are court-ordered; whether the payments have consistently been made on time; the length of time the applicant has been receiving the payments; the financial situation of the person making the payments; the applicant's ability to compel payment if necessary
3. 15
4. true; true; false
5. the applicant's tax returns for the previous two years, and possibly audited financial statements as well

Exercise 13C

1. Usually Acceptable: a, b, e, f, h
   Usually Unacceptable: c, d, g
2. income that meets the lender's standards for quality and durability
3. If the applicant has been making a living through temporary work in the same field for a number of years, it would probably be treated as self-employment income.
4. none of these would be included unless the family member was a co-applicant for the loan
5. false

Exercise 13D

1. $3,033
2. a. housing expense
   d. income ratios
   e. W2 form
   b. income durability
   c. income quality
3. housing expense; debt
4. principal; interest; taxes; insurance
5. true; false; false

Exercise 13E

1. liabilities; assets
2. liquid assets
3. gift; borrowed; gift letter
4. c. reserves
   d. liabilities
   b. assets
   e. liquid assets
   a. net equity
5. a Request for Verification of Deposit

Exercise 13F

1. slow payments; bill consolidation or refinancing; collections; repossessions; foreclosures; judgments; bankruptcies
2. seven; Chapter 7 and Chapter 11 bankruptcies
3. false; false; false
4. 1. the problems occurred during a specific time period for an understandable reason
   2. prior and subsequent credit ratings have been good

Exercise 14A

1. Fannie Mae (FNMA); Freddie Mac (FHLMC)
2. amortized
3. true; false; true
4. longer
5. a balloon payment

Exercise 14B

1. d. nonconforming loan
   e. conventional loan
   f. fully amortized loan
   b. partially amortized loan
   c. 30-year loan
   a. 15-year loan
2. b, d
3. b, c
4. The shorter loan term reduces the lenders risk, so the lender is willing to accept a lower return.
5. b

Exercise 14C

1. fixed-rate
2. a, c, d
3. 1. interest rate cap
   2. payment cap
4. d. margin
   a. negative amortization
   e. index
   b. conversion option
   c. rate adjustment period
5. true; false; true
6. a feature in an ARM that allows the borrower to convert the loan to a fixed rate loan at some time during the loan term

Exercise 14D

1. loan amount; sales price; appraised value
2. 87%; 90%
3. b, c
4. All three are correct
5. lender; default and foreclosure

Exercise 14E

1. $1,500
2. 1. origination fees
   2. discount points
3. discount points
4. are high
5. 1. lowers monthly payment
   2. helps buyer qualify for loan (because lower payment used for underwriting)

Exercise 14F

1. more than ten
2. b. 28%
   a. 33%
   c. 36%
3. $460
4. two
5. $5,000

Exercise 14G

1. closing costs
2. 30; 15
3. Mutual Mortgage Insurance Plan; 203(b)
   1. The property must contain no more than 4 units.
   2. The borrower must occupy one of the units as his or her primary residence.
4. easier qualifying standards; lower downpayments; financing of closing costs; no prepayment penalties
5. true; false; true; true; false

Exercise 14H

1. false; false; true; false; true
2. secondary financing
3. easier; 41%
4. 1. The total of the loans may not exceed the base loan amount.
   2. The borrower must qualify on the basis of the combined payments for both loans.
   3. Payments on the second loan must be monthly, and in roughly equal amounts.

4. There can be no balloon payment on the second loan for at least 10 years.
5. There can be no prepayment penalty on the second loan.

5. a. effective income
   b. housing expense to income ratio
   c. fixed payment to income ratio
   d. MIP

Exercise 14I

1. a
2. true; false; false; true
3. 1. The buyer who assumes the loan must be an eligible vet who is willing to substitute his or her entitlement for that of the seller.
   2. The assumptor must meed VA credit guidelines.
   3. The loan payments must be current.
4. 1. The combined loan amounts may not exceed the appraised value of the property.
   2. The buyer's income must qualify for the combined loan payments.
   3. The interest rate on the second loan may not exceed the rate on the VA loan.
   4. The conditions of the second loan may not be more restrictive than those of the VA loan.
5. 2% of the loan amount

Exercise 14J

1. cash flow
2. CONVENTIONAL: c, d
   FHA-INSURED: b, f
   VA-GUARANTEED: a, e
3. the total obligations to income ratio; 41%
4. 1. the size of the loan
   2. the size of the vet's family
   3. the location of the property (geographical region)
5. true; false; false; true

Exercise 15A

1. fiduciary
2. false
3. an estimate or opinion of value; or the act of estimating value
4. setting a sales price; setting a loan amount; establishing the values of properties in an exchange; estate liquidations; corporate mergers and acquisitions; property tax assessments; bankruptcies; condemnations; property management (setting rental rates); land development (identifying highest and best use); etc.
5. the Uniform Standards of Professional Appraisal Practice

Exercise 15B

1. b., d. utility value
   a. market value
   c. market price
2. arm's length
3. market value
4. the Uniform Standards of Professional Appraisal Practice
5. false; true; false

Exercise 15C

1. change
2. the use that would bring the owner the greatest net return
3. 1. social ideals and standards
   2. economic fluctuations
   3. government regulations
4. 1. integration or development
   2. equilibrium
   3. disintegration
   4. rejuvenation or revitalization
5. true; false; false

Exercise 15D

1. e. highest and best use
   h. change
   f. supply and demand
   a. substitution
   b. conformity
   c. contribution
   g. anticipation
   d. competition
2. progression; regression
3. b
4. false; false; true

Exercise 15E

1. NEIGHBORHOOD ANALYSIS: d, e, g
   SITE ANALYSIS: b, c, f
   BUILDING ANALYSIS: a
2. indicators
3. 1. define the problem
   2. determine what data are needed and where to find them
   3. gather and verify general data
   4. gather and verify specific data
   5. select and apply valuation method(s)
   6. reconcile value indicators for final estimate of value
   7. issue appraisal report
4. a, c, d
5. general data; specific data

Exercise 15F

1. six months
2. location
3. 1. sales comparison approach
   2. cost approach
   3. income approach
4. Values are constantly changing, so past sales prices are not likely to represent present property values unless the sales were fairly recent in time.
5. a

Exercise 15G

1. false
2. three
3. 1. date of sale
   2. location
   3. physical characteristics
   4. terms of sale
4. not use the sale as one of the comparables for the appraisal

Exercise 15H

1. a. replacement cost
   b. reproduction cost
2. replacement

3.
   1. the square foot method
   2. the unit-in-place method
   3. the quantity survey method
4.
   1. deferred maintenance
   2. functional obsolescence
   3. external obsolescence
5. external obsolescence
6. depreciation
7. sales comparison

Exercise 15I

1. c. economic rent
   d. contract rent
   a. effective gross income
   b. net income
2. c
3. Mortgage payments (debt service) are not deducted from effective gross income in calculating net income, because they are not considered operating expenses for appraisal purposes.
4. Annual Net Income ÷ Capitalization Rate = Value
5. $95,000
6. higher

Exercise 15J

1. true
2. monthly rent
3. reconcile; market
4. Uniform Residential Appraisal

Exercise 16A

1.
   1. escrow instructions
   2. gives his or her consent
2. is already representing one of the parties; charge a separate fee for those services
3. both (An escrow agent is a dual agent.)
4. a certified escrow agent
5. true; true; true

Exercise 16B

1. buyer's credits; seller's credits
2. as a debit to the buyer and a credit to the seller
3.
   1. the escrow instructions
   2. the terms of the purchase and sale agreement
   3. local customs
4. debit; credits
5. false; true; true

Exercise 16C

1. the payoff of the loan; any prepayment penalty; the reserve account balance; the lender
2. buyer
3. $145,000, debited to buyer and credited to seller
4. a credit to the buyer and a debit to the seller
5. as a debit to the seller

Exercise 16D

1. Buyer's Debits: a
   Buyer's Credits: b, d, f
   Seller's Debits: c, e, f
   Seller's Credits: a
2. 1. the deed from seller to buyer (fee paid by buyer)
   2. the buyer's new mortgage or deed of trust (fee paid by buyer)
   3. the satifaction of mortgage or deed of reconveyance for the seller's existing mortgage or deed of trust (fee paid by seller)
3. seller; buyer
4. bill of sale
5. The fee is usually split 50/50 between the buyer and seller.

Exercise 16E

1. b
2. 1. determine the per diem rate
   2. determine the number of days for which the party is responsible for the expense
   3. multiply the per diem rate times the number of days
3. false (With the widespread use of calculators and computers, there is no reason not to prorate on the basis of the exact number of days in a month or year.)
4. Jan 31; Feb 28 or 29; Mar 31; Apr 30; May 31; Jun 30; Jul 31; Aug 31; Sep 30; Oct 31; Nov 30; Dec 31
5. 5

Exercise 16F

1. $160.00
2. $349.32 credit to seller and debit to buyer (60 days at $5.82192 per diem)
3. a
4. $253.15 (336 days at $0.75342 per diem)

Exercise 16G

1. August 1 through August 15; October; August 16 through August 31
2. $174.80 (9 days at $19.42259 per diem)
3. b
4. $1,139.18 (28 days at $40.68493 per diem)
5. September 1

Exercise 16H

1. $11,503.55
2. $49,867.74
3. The seller will need to pay the difference in cash in order to close the transaction.
4. 1. the loan balance
   2. any unpaid interest on the loan
   3. any prepayment penalty that may apply
   4. any balance in the seller's reserve account
   5. the recording fee for the satisfaction of mortgage or deed of reconveyance

5. purchase price; property taxes (prorated); seller financing; assumption of seller's loan; recording fees; attorney fees; escrow fee; prorated rent (for income property)

Exercise 16I

1. b, c
2. a, b, c
3. 1099-S; name; social security number; gross sales proceeds; broker
4. one business day
5. anyone connected with the sale, including the real estate agents
6. false; true; false

Exercise 17A

1. value; tenants
2. 1. supply and value of money
   2. trends in occupancy rates
   3. market rental rates
   4. employment levels
   5. family size and life styles
3. A technical oversupply means there are more units than consumers (potential tenants). In an economic oversupply, there are enough consumers, but the consumers can't afford to pay current levels of rent.
4. Higher occupancy levels cause property values to increase, while lower occupancy levels decrease property values.
5. true; true; true; true

Exercise 17B

1. 1. residential
   2. office
   3. retail
   4. industrial
2. residential property; industrial
3. a price per square foot of leased space
4. The amount of rent for a retail lease often depends on the income of the tenant businesses, and the right mix of tenants can result in higher income for all of them.
5. true; false; false

Exercise 17C

1. true; true; false
2. All the listed points should be included in the agreement.
3. how often the manager will report to the owner, and how detailed the reports will be
4. The management agreement is the contract between the owner and the manager; the management plan is an outline of the manager's strategy for managing the property.
5. the owner's goals for the property

Exercise 17D

1. 1. regional analysis
   2. neighborhood analysis
   3. property analysis
   4. market analysis

2. government and trade group publications
3. true; true; true
4. a, d, e

Exercise 17E

1. defining the market for the property
2. to see how the property compares to competing properties in the market, and identify trends in occupancy levels and rental rates
3. number of available units in the area; average age and character of comparable buildings; quality of average unit available in the market; number of potential tenants in the market; current rental rates for comparable units; current occupancy levels for comparable units
4. true; false; false

Exercise 17F

1. a rental schedule
2. fixed expenses; variable expenses
3. The management plan is the manager's strategy for implementing the owner's goals; the management proposal is a draft of the management plan, and becomes the management plan when accepted by the owner.
4. false; true; false
5. vacancies and bad debts

Exercise 17G

1. 1. leasing and tenant relations
   2. manager/owner relations
   3. property maintenance
2. newspaper classified advertising
3. broadcast advertising (radio and TV)
4. false; false; false
5. careful selection and qualification of tenants

Exercise 17H

1. e. rent roll
   d. statement of operations
   a. summary of operations
   c. rent schedule
   b. statement of disbursements
2. a letter explaining the various elements of a statement of operations
3. false; false; false
4. b, d, e
5. income is significantly lower than projected, or expenses are significantly higher than projected

Exercise 17I

1. d. preventive maintenance
   b. corrective maintenance
   a. housekeeping
   c. new construction
2. Preventive maintenance is performed to maintain the condition of the property, while corrective maintenance is performed to correct actual defects in the property.
3. 1. inventory the property's equipment and physical elements
   2. prepare a schedule of inspections and maintenance
   3. maintain records of inspections, maintenance, and improvements

4. maintenance employees or independent contractors

Exercise 18A

1. The tax credit is more valuable, since it directly reduces the taxpayer's tax liability; a tax deduction merely reduces the amount of income that is subject to tax.
2. true; false; true
3. 1. personal use
   2. investment purposes
4. 1. losses in connection with the taxpayer's trade or business
   2. losses on transactions entered for profit
   3. casualty or theft losses
5. any economic benefit realized by a taxpayer

Exercise 18B

1. c. deduction
   e. tax credit
   d. income
   b. initial basis
   a. capital asset
2. $173,500
3. realized; recognized
4. adjusted basis
5. true; true; true; true

Exercise 18C

1. d. principal residence
   e. personal use property
   c. property held for the production of income
   f. unimproved investment property
   b. property used in a trade or business
   a. dealer property
2. less than 100% of the sales price
3. a, c, d, e
4. 248,000 x 6% = 14,880
   248,000 – 155,400 – 14,880 – 3,320 = 74,400 gross profit
   74,400 ÷ 248,000 = 30% gross profit ratio
   25,000 + 1,045.75 = 26,045.75 principal received
   26,045.75 x 30% = 7,813.73 taxable principal
   7,813.73 + 5,954.25 = 13,767.98 total taxable income
5. true

Exercise 18D

1. two years
2. 55
3. 145,000 – 11,000 = 134,000 amount realized
   Amount realized is less than cost of new home, so no tax is due on the first sale.
4. 134,000 – 120,000 = 14,000 deferred gain on first sale
   135,000 – 14,000 = 121,000 basis in new home
5. false; false; true

Exercise 18E

1. true; true; false
2. boot
3. $125,000 ($62,500 for a married taxpayer filing separately)
4. mortgage relief, a form of boot
5. installment sales deferral; rollover on sale of principal residence or involuntary conversion; tax-deferred exchange; exemption on sale of personal residence by taxpayer aged 55 or more

Exercise 18F

1. cost recovery (or depreciation); b, c
2. depreciable
3. b, c
4. 1. $1,000,000
   2. $100,000

   the size of the loan
5. Repairs simply keep the property in ordinary, efficient operating condition, while capital expenditures add to the value of the property and prolong its economic life. Repairs expenses are generally deductible in the year incurred, while capital expenditures must be added to the basis.

Exercise 19A

1. Civil Rights; Fair
2. The court could order an injunction against the defendant, and could order the defendant to pay compensatory and punitive damages.
3. The Act prohibited discrimination in programs that involved federal financial assistance, but failed to cover most FHA and VA loan programs.
4. true; true; true
5. 1. race
   2. color
   3. religion
   4. sex
   5. national origin
   6. handicap
   7. familial status

Exercise 19B

1. b. blockbusting
   a. redlining
   c. steering
2. b, c, d
3. the Home Mortgage Disclosure Act of 1975
4. 1. the owner does not own more than 3 such homes
   2. no real estate agent is employed in the transaction
   3. no discriminatory advertising is used
5. four

Exercise 19C

1. 18 years old
2. older
3. true; false; false
4. 1. properties developed under a government program to assist the elderly
   2. properties intended for and solely occupied by persons age 62 or older
   3. properties intended for older persons and designed to meet their needs, if at least 80% of the units are occupied by at least one person age 55 or older

5. a physical or mental impairment that substantially limits one or more major life activities

Exercise 19D

1. Housing and Urban Development; Fair Housing and Equal Opportunity
2. 1. file a complaint with HUD
   2. file a lawsuit in federal court
   3. file a lawsuit in state court
3. Washington Human Rights Commission
4. false; true; false

Exercise 19E

1. an individual; personal, family or household
2. true; false; false
3. public accommodation
4. a, b, c
5. b

Exercise 19F

1. none
2. true
3. six months after the alleged discrimination took place
4. 1. license suspension or revocation
   2. a fine of up to $1,000 for each offense
   3. mandatory course work in civil rights and nondiscriminatory real estate practices
   4. criminal prosecution for gross misdemeanor
5. false (However, even though this practice is prohibited by the law, the Human Rights Commission has ruled that it will not hear complaints on this basis.)

Exercise 20A

1. reinforced concrete
2. d. stud
   a. rafter
   e. joist
   c. sheathing
   b. siding
   f. plate
3. c
4. to automatically cut off the supply of electricity to a circuit in the event of an overload, which could cause a fire
5. resist heat transfer; higher
6. 1. chemical treatment of the soil around the house
   2. chemical treatment of wood in contact with the foundation or ground
   3. metal shields between the foundation and superstructure

Exercise 20B

1. less; because rents tend to increase with inflation, while mortgage payments (not including taxes and insurance) do not
2. renting
3. 1. deductability of mortgage interest
   2. deductability of property taxes

4. true; true; true
5. 1. Part of the mortgage payment goes to pay off the principal amount of the loan, which increases the buyer's equity.
   2. Any appreciation in the value of the home will also increase the buyer's equity.

Exercise 20C

1. The value of a home is affected by the values of the homes in the surrounding neighborhood, and owner-occupied properties tend to hold their value better than rental properties.
2. lot size, lot shape, slope, soil stability, drainage, view, etc.
3. three
4. a, b, e, f
5. a, b, c, d, e

Exercise 20D

1. liquidity; safety; yield
2. true; false; false; true
3. equity
4. by taking out a home equity loan
5. Through leverage (using borrowed funds to purchase a property), the investor can achieve a higher rate of appreciation than that of the property itself.
6. appreciation in value of the asset; positive cash flow from the property

Exercise 21A

1. B = A ÷ C
2. Read the question and understand what you are looking for.
3. Divide the top number of the fraction (the numerator) by the bottom number (the denominator).
4. six
5. none (Simply enter the numbers as they appear, including the decimal point, and perform the desired operation.)

Exercise 21B

1. rectangle: area = length x width

   triangle: area = 1/2 x base x height
2. Convert feet to yards or yards to feet so that both dimensions are in the same unit of measurement.
3. 102,400 (320 x 320)
4. Divide the figure into component rectangles and triangles, find the areas of the components, and add them together.

Exercise 21C

1. Percentage x Total = Part
2. 325 (3.25 x 100)
3. Divide the amount of the commission by the commission rate. (Total = Part ÷ Percentage)
4. Convert six months to 0.5 years (or convert 12% per year to 1% per month), so that the figures for Rate and Time are in equivalent units.
5. Divide the amount of interest by the annual rate times the number of years. (Principal = Interest ÷ (Rate x Time))

Exercise 21D

1. nothing (It's the same formula; only the names of the variables are different.)
2. 100 ÷ 1 = 100;
   100 = 10,000%;
   10,000% - 100% = 9,900%
3. operating expenses, and an allowance for vacancies and bad debts
4. Leap years (366 days) are evenly divisible by 4 (e.g., 1996 ÷ 4 = 499).
5. more (A lower capitalization rate results in a higher value for the same amount of income.)

Exercise 22A

1. five
2. for a commission or other compensation
3. business opportunities
4. a, b, c, d, e, f
5. 1. to insure that real estate agents have a minimum level of competence in handling real estate transactions
   2. to regulate the business activities of real estate agents

Exercise 22B

1. is not going to receive compensation for her work; attorney in fact
2. a, c
3. designated
4. a, b, d
5. b, c

Exercise 22C

1. one year; pass the exam again
2. 120; 5
   1. real estate law
   2. brokerage management
   3. business management
3. a, b, c, d, e
4. true; false; true; false; false
5. a

Exercise 22D

1. false; true; false
2. 30; 20
3. b
4. 30; real esate practices
5. a

Exercise 23A

1. the broker that the salesperson is affiliated with (and, if the salesperson works at a branch office, the branch manager as well)
2. surrendered to the Director of the Dept. of Licensing; affiliated with another broker
3. a licensed broker who allows someone else to operate a brokerage under his or her license.
4. true; false; true
5. notify the Department of Licensing in writing

Exercise 23B

1. true; false; false; true
2. blind ad; is
3. a, c, d
4. trust account; registered location
5. the main office; the offices where the licensee's work

Exercise 23C

1. d. blind ad
   e. inactive licensee
   f. fee broker
   c. pooled trust account
   b. transaction folder
   a. separate trust account
2. c
3. never
4. false; false; true; true
5. the first banking day after the broker receives the funds

Exercise 23D

1. Suzanne Potter of Haven Real Estate, Inc.
   Ken Balmer
   Hannah Cohen of Cohen Realty, Inc.
   Claude Jansen
2. the seller signs the buyer's offer
3. the end of the first banking day following receipt

   If the purchase and sale agreement instructs the agent to hold the check until the buyer's offer has been accepted; or if the agreement provides that someone other than the broker (such as a closing agent) will hold the deposit until closing.
4. true; false; false
5. the broker who first receives the earnest money deposit

Exercise 23E

1. c, e
2. true; true; true
3. b
4. is
5. the broker is designated as the closing agent in the purchase and sale agreement

Exercise 23F

1. true; false; true; true; true
2. cease and desist order
3. 1. require Hatter to pay a fine (up to $1,000)
   2. require Hatter to take a class that covers trust fund procedures
4. 20 days; a verified statement of the charges
5. 30 days; $500